SIMPLY GÖDEL

SIMPLY GÖDEL

RICHARD TIESZEN

Simply Charly

New York

Simply Charly
5 Columbus Circle, 8th Fl
New York, NY 10019
www.simplycharly.com

ISBN: 978-1-943657-15-5

Contents

Praise for *Simply Gödel*

"Tieszen's *Simply Gödel* is a remarkable achievement—a handy guide with the impact of a philosophical tome. It's all here: elegantly lucid discussions of Kurt Gödel's epochal discoveries, a sympathetic account of the eccentric genius's life, focused discussions of his encounters with his astonished peers, and a visionary peek into the future of mathematics, philosophy, and the on-rushing specter of robots with minds. A compact masterpiece, brimming with fresh revelations."
—Rudy Rucker, author of *Infinity and the Mind*

"It's almost impossible to get the balance right—of Gödel's mathematics, his philosophy, and life. But this amazing new addition to the Gödel canon offers an accessible and engaging account of his incompleteness theorems, his work and his friendship with Einstein, and so much more. It also offers an account of how philosophy and philosophical concerns provide an underpinning for much of his work."
—Errol Morris, Oscar-award winning director of *The Fog of War* **as well as** *The Thin Blue Line* **and** *A Brief History of Time*

"This book meets the challenge of providing a concise yet cogent non-technical overview of Gödel's life and work, which should help to clarify to laymen why Gödel has become famous and what his incompleteness theorems do and do not say."
—John W. Dawson, author of *Logical Dilemmas: The Life and Work of Kurt Gödel* **and Professor Emeritus of Mathematics at Penn State York**

"I think *Simply Gödel* is a success. It doesn't talk down to its readers, but challenges them to come up to the task of trying to grasp what Gödel achieved. It combines sober, fair-minded caution in presenting Gödel's formal results in a variety of fields with an evident sympathy for Gödel's philosophy of "Platonic rationalism"—which according to Gödel both underlies and is suggested by his mathematical results—a combination that, sadly, is all too rarely found."

—**Palle Yourgrau, author of** *A World Without Time: The Forgotten Legacy of Gödel and Einstein* **and Harry A. Wolfson Professor of Philosophy at Brandeis University**

"Kurt Gödel, as a very young researcher in the 1930s, found three very major results that set the stage for extensive developments in contemporary logic, the philosophy of mathematics, and theoretical computer science. Tieszen's lucid style sets out the facts and the history of Gödel's work, life and influence. This book is an admirable accomplishment, which also helps explain the intellectual and philosophical environment in which Gödel's ideas developed."

—**Dana S. Scott, Emeritus University Professor of Mathematical Logic at Carnegie Mellon University**

"As a first guide to Gödel's universe, I heartily recommend the reflection of it that Tieszen presents in *Simply Gödel*. Highly readable, surveyable, and dependable, it testifies to Tieszen's great gift for teaching."

—**Mark van Atten, author of** *Essays on Gödel's Reception of Leibniz, Husserl, and Brouwer,* **and Senior Researcher at CNRS, Paris, France**

Other *Great Lives* Titles

Series Editor's Foreword

Simply Charly's "Great Lives" series offers brief but authoritative introductions to the world's most influential people—scientists, artists, writers, economists, and other historical figures whose contributions have had a meaningful and enduring impact on our society.

Each book provides an illuminating look at the works, ideas, personal lives, and the legacies these individuals left behind, also shedding light on the thought processes, specific events and experiences that led these remarkable people to their groundbreaking discoveries or other achievements. Additionally, every volume explores various challenges they had to face and overcome to make history in their respective fields, as well as the little-known character traits, quirks, strengths and frailties, myths and controversies that sometimes surrounded these personalities.

Our authors are prominent scholars and other top experts who have dedicated their careers to exploring each facet of their subjects' work and personal lives.

Unlike many other works that are merely descriptions of the major milestones in a person's life, the "Great Lives" series goes above and beyond the standard format and content. It brings substance, depth, and clarity to the sometimes-complex lives and works of history's most powerful and influential people.

We hope that by exploring this series, readers will not only gain new knowledge and understanding of what drove these geniuses, but also find inspiration for their own lives. Isn't this what a great book is supposed to do?

Charles Carlini, Simply Charly
New York City

Preface

Kurt Gödel is regarded as one of the most important logicians of all time. The brilliant polymath John von Neumann called him "the greatest logician since Aristotle." Gödel's incompleteness theorems, in particular, have, like certain other bold, scientific achievements, filtered into popular culture to some extent. His work, however, is still not as widely known as that of other scientists such as Albert Einstein, Niels Bohr, Werner Heisenberg, Stephen Hawking, Francis Crick and James Watson. That could be because Gödel never sought to popularize his work. Unlike Einstein, who later became his close friend, he was never besieged by a public that sought autographs, photographs, and correspondence. When scholars, students, and others did write to him, he often did not respond. Far from being a celebrity, he was a very reserved man who seemed to have no interest whatsoever in being in the public eye. Almost all of the writing that he published during his lifetime was highly technical and precise, expressed in the formulas of mathematical logic and physics, and thus inaccessible to all but those people who worked in his fields of research. This fact poses special challenges to those who wish to make Gödel's ideas understandable to a wider educated public.

My goal in this book is to present Gödel's most important ideas to a general audience but with a minimal use of mathematical notation. I think such notation cannot be avoided altogether because without it there can be no understanding of some of his central ideas. Details of Gödel's life are of interest, but his genius can be best glimpsed through his ideas. I endeavor to steer clear of the forests of technical symbols one finds in reading many of Gödel's papers and notes. I believe it is possible to simplify some of his most difficult logical work and that such simplification has its virtues, but *over*simplification can lead to serious misunderstandings. The trick is to find the right balance between simplification and oversimplification, and I hope to have achieved that in the short space of this book. In parts where a little bit of logical or mathematical notation is used, I urge the reader to seek at least some sense of what is going on. It is not necessary to obtain a perfect grasp. If these few sections of the book seem opaque, then I suggest just skipping over them and reading the explanations in colloquial English that usually surround them.

We are still learning about Gödel's views, based on a more thorough examination of items in his literary estate. These include a wealth of material that he did not publish during his lifetime in papers, lectures, correspondence, and notebooks inscribed in shorthand. Presentations on his life and work are thus to some extent still time-sensitive, owing to the fact that not all of his ideas have been thoroughly plumbed. Gödel's mathematical, philosophical and theological notebooks, for example, are written in a now obsolete form of shorthand that has only recently been tackled by scholars. It will probably be a while before the complete picture of Gödel emerges. Although this is a short book, it covers some topics that had not been included in earlier treatments of his contributions but about which we now have more information. This especially includes material on his philosophy and his philosophical heroes Plato, Gottfried Leibniz and Edmund Husserl. I include this material to give the reader a better understanding of the range of Gödel's interests and achievements.

Unlike the vast majority of results in the fields of formal logic and mathematics, Gödel's technical findings are remarkable for almost always having philosophical significance. Most results in the fields of formal logic and mathematics are not like this. In Gödel's case, this was a consequence of the fact that his thinking from early on was influenced by philosophical ideas. As he said to the logician Hao Wang, "I was always out for important results and found it better to think than to publish." In his work, we have a true combination of philosophy and mathematics.

The content of Gödel's logical and mathematical work is pure and beautiful but, as will be seen, his life was often filled with suffering due to physical and mental health problems. The contrast between his work and private life is profound. In this book I present many of Gödel's philosophical ideas, along with biographical particulars of his life—early years with his family, university days, his move to the Institute for Advanced Study in Princeton, emotional problems, and the sad details of his later life—as well as an overview of the remarkable body of work that he produced in logic, physics, and even rational theology. The goal is to see the whole of Gödel but in relatively short form and in chronological order, with attention to how his life and work were sometimes interwoven with enthusiasm and fulfillment but at other times torturously.

Richard Tieszen
San José, CA

Acknowledgements

For biographical information, I have relied on a number of sources. I am indebted to John Dawson's definitive biography, *Logical Dilemmas: The Life and Work of Kurt Gödel*. This book is highly recommended to anyone who wants to learn more about Gödel's life and work. I also relied on Hao Wang's *Reflections on Kurt Gödel* and *A Logical Journey*. I was very fortunate to have discussed Gödel's views on logic, mathematics, and philosophy with Wang from 1985 until 1993. Other important biographical sources that were consulted include Solomon Feferman's "Gödel's Life and Work," Georg Kreisel's "Kurt Gödel, 28 April 1906 – 14 January 1978," Curt Christian's "Leben und Wirken Kurt Gödels," and Karl Sigmund's "Dozent Gödel Will Not Lecture."

I have benefitted from participation in the multi-year project *Kurt Gödel: Philosopher-Scientist,* which has been dedicated to transcribing, analyzing and publishing Gödel's philosophical notebooks, known as the Max-Phil notebooks. This project was directed by Professor Gabriella Crocco.

Lastly, thanks to the Zen Hospice Project in San Francisco and to Samuel Domingo in particular.

1

Early Years

Throughout his career, Kurt Gödel was described as a shy, solemn, introverted, and very courteous man, but one who lacked warmth and sensitivity. He is typically pictured as otherworldly, anorexic, and a hypochondriac. Short and slight of build, he was said to be frail and plagued by mental and physical health problems. Gödel was very cautious about letting his philosophical views be known, often withholding work and not responding to correspondents, even though he would draft replies. There was nothing reserved, however, about his work in logic and the foundations of mathematics. His ideas in these fields burst upon the scene like supernovae. He was impossible to ignore. Much of what he published displayed outright genius and, as it happens, the same could be said for much of what he wrote but did not publish during his lifetime. His remarkable incompleteness theorems were published when he was only 25 years old. Two years prior to that, he had proved his completeness theorem in his doctoral thesis. He had obviously mastered a lot of work in mathematical logic at any early age. In what was a sign of things to come, young Kurt had been nicknamed *Herr Warum*—Mr. Why—by his family because of his inquisitiveness.

Adolescence

Kurt Friedrich Gödel was born on April 28, 1906, in Brünn, now Brno, in the Austro-Hungarian province of Moravia. The local population was mostly Czech but included a substantial German-speaking minority, to which Gödel's parents belonged. Brünn was a major textile center, which was why Gödel's father, Rudolf, had moved there from Vienna. The family of Kurt's mother, Marianne, had moved from the Rhineland for the same reason. Rudolf and Marianne had two sons. Kurt was the younger by four years. His older brother Rudolf was the source of various anecdotes about Kurt and much of the available information about the Gödel family history.

Kurt's father was an energetic, inventive, and self-made man who became a director and then part owner of one of Brünn's main textile firms. Kurt's mother attended a French school in Brünn and received a broad literary education; she was more cultured and better educated than her husband. The family of Kurt's father had been Old Catholic, followers of a dissident sect that split from the Roman church in the mid-1800s, but Rudolf senior was not observant. Gödel's mother was Lutheran, and though the Gödels had their boys baptized in the Lutheran Church, the family was not especially religious. Kurt developed a stronger interest in religion than the other family members, but he was never a member of any congregation. He said he was a believer, "*theistic*, not pantheistic (following Leibniz rather than Spinoza)." He was very circumspect about publicly expressing religious beliefs, but later in life, he made a number of interesting observations about religion in letters to his mother. He also wrote a purely formal, logical "proof" for the existence of God.

According to his brother, Kurt's childhood was mostly cheerful, although he was timid and could be easily upset. Rudolf described periods of happy and tranquil play, with building blocks, a train set, and tin soldiers. At about the age of 5, according to his brother, Kurt had a slight anxiety neurosis, which later disappeared completely. It is interesting that this occurred so early, given Gödel's later mental disabilities. At some point between the ages of 7 and 9, Kurt contracted rheumatic fever, apparently a fairly severe case. For the rest of his life, he believed this illness had damaged his heart, even though this was never established medically. His brother said this early illness was a source of Gödel's longtime concern with his health, which bordered on hypochondria. Other acquaintances have asserted that Gödel was a full-blown hypochondriac. This early illness may also have been linked to his later distrust of doctors.

At the age of 6, Kurt was enrolled at the *Evangelische Volksschule*, a Lutheran school in Brünn. From 1916 to 1924 he attended the

Deutsches Staats-Realgymnasium, where he was an outstanding student. He earned the highest grades in all of his subjects, excelling especially in mathematics, languages, and religion. Only once did he receive less than the highest mark, somewhat surprisingly in mathematics. His literary estate preserves some of his precise work in geometry from that time, along with his report cards from elementary and secondary school. He learned to play chess and, according to his brother, "was very eager to win and very wretched or vexed when he lost, which rarely happened." It was also during his time in secondary school that he learned Gabelsberger shorthand, so named after its creator Franz Xaver Gabelsberger. Gödel used this system, now obsolete, in many of his later notebooks. Portions of these, on philosophy, mathematics, and theology, have only recently been transcribed and their contents could prove quite valuable to scholars.

Gödel said his interest in mathematics began when he was around 14 or 15, stimulated by an introductory calculus book. Soon after that, in 1922, he first read the great philosopher Immanuel Kant (1724-1804). Kant's philosophy was to have a lasting impact on Gödel, although he stated on several occasions that he was never a Kantian. He also read widely outside of his school's curriculum.

His brother related how Kurt often stayed home with a book when the rest of the family went out for walks. His father was not especially happy with this, thinking the boy was too bookish. As Kurt became more concerned with his health, he became less interested in the physical activities he had once enjoyed.

Although World War I was raging during Kurt's early school years, it had little direct effect on his family. Brünn was removed from the main action of the war and was untouched by the devastation that left such a terrible mark elsewhere in Europe. What did happen by the war's end in 1918, however, was the collapse of the Austro-Hungarian Empire and the absorption of Moravia into the new nation of Czechoslovakia. Brünn became Brno. The changes after the war did have some adverse effects on the German-speaking minority but the Gödels were able to carry on much as they did before and were able to settle into a comfortable villa before long.

To the University of Vienna

Gödel went to the University of Vienna after graduating from the *Gymnasium* in 1924. His brother had been studying medicine there since 1920. A lifelong bachelor, Rudolf became a radiologist and practiced in Vienna for his entire life. Kurt was to live in Vienna for the next 15 years, punctuated in the 1930s with trips to the United States. It was during his time in Austria's capital that he produced most of the work for which he is now famous. Especially in the years 1929 to 1939, he worked intensely, proving his major results in mathematical logic. Despite undergoing tumultuous changes between the wars, Vienna remained rich in culture and intellectual activity. This was the city of Sigmund Freud and the psychoanalytic movement, of the Vienna Circle and the philosopher Ludwig Wittgenstein (1889-1951), and of a host of famous writers, composers, poets, and architects.

Gödel was at first undecided between the study of mathematics and physics, initially leaning toward the latter. It was evidently the precision of mathematics that ultimately led him to choose it. Some of his professors may have influenced this decision, too. Later, in a document known as the Grandjean questionnaire, Gödel wrote that he had been a "conceptual and mathematical realist since about 1925." "Realism" also goes by the name of "Platonism," and it will be examined in more detail shortly. The Grandjean questionnaire is an important source of information about Gödel's interests. The sociologist Burke Grandjean sent it to Gödel in 1974. Gödel filled out the questionnaire, probably in 1975, but never returned it. It was found after his death along with many other unsent letters and withheld items.

One of Gödel's fellow university students, Olga Taussky-Todd (1906-1995), met him in 1925 at a seminar given by the philosopher Moritz Schlick (1882-1936). Schlick was at the center of the group that came to be known as the Vienna Circle. The seminar was on the *Introduction to Mathematical Philosophy* published in 1919 by the British philosopher and logician Bertrand Russell (1872-1970). Taussky-Todd reported that Gödel hardly ever spoke at the seminar but was quick to see problems and offer solutions. In spite of being very reserved, others could see that he was exceptionally talented. Taussky-Todd said his help was much in demand and always readily offered. He was always very clear about what was at issue and explained things slowly and calmly. She also mentioned that Kurt "had a liking for members of the opposite sex, and he made no secret of this fact." Although anti-Semitism was rife in Austria, Taussky-Todd said Kurt had a friendly attitude toward Jews. He himself wrote that this was true of his entire family. There were times in the 1930s and 1940s, however, when he seemed oblivious to the plight of European Jews. He was apolitical, and his apparent insensitivity can perhaps be traced to what some have called his otherworldliness. It may also have been due to his focus on his own mental and physical problems.

Others around him in Vienna reported that he was unusually quiet but that when he did speak, he was calm, expressed himself very clearly and precisely, and displayed great talent in mathematics. He was not asocial in these early years. In fact, his student days in Vienna were very fruitful and seemed to have been enjoyable. For example, he spent significant time in coffeehouses, which were central to Viennese cultural and intellectual life.

The Vienna Circle

In 1926, Gödel began meeting with the members of the Vienna Circle, to whom he was introduced by the mathematician Hans Hahn (1879-1934). The Circle came to be identified with the philosophy known as "logical positivism" or "logical empiricism." Apart from Schlick and Hahn, some of the Circle's other main figures who would become influential were Rudolf Carnap (1891-1970), Otto Neurath, Herbert Feigl, Friedrich Waismann, Philipp Frank, Felix Kaufmann, and Karl Menger (1902-1985), who would become Gödel's longtime friend. Hahn acted as Gödel's doctoral thesis advisor, overseeing Gödel's *Habilitationschrift*, a kind of second, "higher" thesis, required to teach in German-speaking universities. In his doctoral thesis, Gödel obtained his first major result in logic, the completeness theorem for what is called predicate logic. Then, in his *Habilitationschrift,* he proved his famous incompleteness theorems. During the Circle's heyday, Kurt stayed in contact with Carnap. In the Grandjean questionnaire, Gödel lists Carnap's lectures on metalogic as an important influence on his completeness and incompleteness papers. Carnap's work, in fact, would play an important role in Gödel's thinking for many years, but often as a foil for developing his own philosophical views on mathematics and logic. He said he never accepted Carnap's view that mathematics was syntax of language, and he even wrote—but never published—six drafts of a paper meant to refute Carnap's position. Later on, he told the logician Hao Wang (1921-1995) that he thought he had succeeded. As we will see, Gödel's argument against Carnap depends directly on his incompleteness theorems.

The Vienna Circle's members held a variety of philosophical positions, but several ideas stood out as central to logical positivism. First, all knowledge was to be analyzed in terms of empirical claims plus logical analysis. Empirical claims are those that can either be verified or refuted by the experience of the senses, as in experiments in natural science. Expressions that are not subject to such verification or refutation should be considered meaningless, as far as questions of knowledge are concerned. Logic, on the other hand, is not supposed to be about objects or to have any content. It consists of linguistic rules or conventions for deducing sentences from one another, determining whether sentences are consistent with one another, and so on, but in itself, logic consists of empty tautologies. Expressions of this type that do not give us any knowledge about the world are said to be "analytic." What happens in sensory experience, in this view, will not affect expressions in logic because they are just the results of our linguistic conventions. In this sense, logical expressions are called "*a priori*" because they are prior to or independent of sense experience. For instance, the expression "All bachelors are unmarried men" would typically be regarded as analytic. An example in formal logic would be "If P, then P" or "If P and Q, then P." Empirical claims, on the other hand, are "synthetic" and "*a posteriori*" because they do have content and give us knowledge about the world only after—posterior to—sense experience. These distinctions between analytic and synthetic, and *a priori* and *a posteriori* have been construed in a host of ways since first introduced in philosophy but this is basically how the logical empiricists understood them. Logic, in this view, is useful and even required for science and knowledge because we use it to organize and unify the empirical, experience-based sentences. The logical positivists also wanted to make philosophy scientific and to reject any of its aspects that couldn't be so regimented. Rejecting metaphysics was a central theme for the Vienna Circle. Members of the group, except for Gödel, typically opposed what they called "metaphysical" positions, including Platonism in particular.

The famous philosopher Ludwig Wittgenstein did not attend the Circle's meetings, but he had a significant impact on its members' views. It seems that while Gödel met with the Circle, he was exposed to Wittgenstein's *Tractatus Logico-Philosophicus*, which Carnap and Schlick were keen on studying in detail. Gödel says he first studied Wittgenstein's writings in 1927 but that he never met Wittgenstein and never read any of his work thoroughly. In 1972, he told Wang he disliked the *Tractatus* because it proposes to show philosophy is impossible. On the whole, Gödel was negative about Wittgenstein's philosophy. Responding to Wittgenstein's opinions about his incompleteness theorems, Gödel had very negative things to say, as we will see in Chapter 6.

Gödel met with the Circle regularly during 1926 through 1928 but then moved away from the group. His own philosophical views were largely antithetical to what the other members believed, and he often took a non-positivistic position in discussions with the Circle's younger members. Speaking of his work from that period, he described "the philosophical consequences of my results, as well as the heuristic principles leading to them, [as] anything but positivistic or empiricistic." As mentioned above, he said he was already a conceptual and mathematical realist by 1925. It is undeniable that the Vienna Circle shaped Gödel in many ways and that it provided him with tremendous intellectual stimulation.

If Gödel was already a Platonic rationalist in 1925, what must it have been like to meet with the Vienna Circle when its members were saying and writing that positions such as Platonism were entirely bankrupt? What is Platonic rationalism anyway? Plato, whom Gödel cited as one of his favorites, thought philosophers should study some mathematics before embarking on philosophical investigations. The idea was that this would prepare the mind to grasp essences or essential truths. In *The Republic*, Book VII, which Gödel may have studied with his professor Heinrich Gomperz in Vienna, Plato wrote:

> What would be the study that would draw the soul away from the world of becoming to the world of being? . . . Geometry and arithmetic would be among the studies we are seeking . . . a philosopher must learn them because he must arise out of the region of generation and lay hold on essence or he can never become a true reckoner . . . they facilitate the conversion of the soul itself from the world of generation to essence and truth . . . they are knowledge of that which always is and not of something which at some time comes into being and passes away.

A standard way to describe Platonic rationalism about mathematics it is to say it accepts the existence of abstract, mind-independent objects and/or truths. A Platonist will say, for example, that natural numbers exist but that they are not the kinds of things that could change, could be in space or time, or could have a cause-and-effect relationship to us. This is what it means to say they are "abstract," as distinct from "concrete." Concrete objects are subject to generation and decay, exist in space and time, and are causally related to us. Platonism holds that mathematical or logical truths are not about things in space or time. Rather, they are "eternally" true. Mathematical objects and truths are discovered, just as we discover new stars, formerly unseen. We didn't invent either the stars or the truths. Mathematical truths, therefore, do not depend on the nature of our minds.

Opposing this idea are several kinds of anti-Platonisms, all of which deny that abstract objects exist independently of the mind. Platonism in logic and mathematics is opposed by forms of "constructivism," which hold that mathematics *does* depend on the human mind and on what the mind can construct in space and/or time. Mathematical truths, in this view, are not eternally true but instead depend on our constructive abilities.

What Platonism says about the existence of objects and/or truths is often accompanied by a rationalist view of knowledge. "Rationalism" is the idea that not all knowledge comes either directly from sense experience or from generalizations from sense experience. Rationalism in philosophy is typically contrasted with "empiricism," which holds that all knowledge *does* come from sense experience. We need to distinguish what we can acquire on the basis of the five senses from the capacity for reason and what reason might allow us to know. A weak form of rationalism says that not all knowledge is derived from sense-experience. A strong form implies that we do not really have any knowledge from sense experience. That is because the senses deceive us or give us information that is fundamentally unclear or uncertain. Clarity, certainty, and knowledge, the rationalist contends, can be acquired only through our ability to reason. Reason might involve rational intuition, as it does in Gödel's thinking, but it also involves our capacity to reason by inference from information at hand. Indeed, the rationalist will argue that only through reason can we know about exactness and perfection. For example, in Euclidean geometry, we learn about points that have no dimension, lines with only one dimension, perfectly straight lines, perfect triangles, perfect spheres, and the like. Furthermore, rationalists often claim that only the capacity for reason allows us to know anything about the infinite or even about the distinction between the infinite and the finite.

The term "intuition" is used in many different ways that can easily lead to misunderstandings. This requires some comment in order to set aside preconceptions. In the rationalist tradition in philosophy, intuition is far from being merely subjective. Just the opposite is true: intuition is required for objectivity. Without intuition of the objects or states of affairs that our thoughts are about, we would have only empty thoughts. Truth requires agreement between what is merely thought and facts that are intuited. Intuition fills in what is merely thought. Some kinds of thoughts can have no corresponding intuitions. For example, we can think about but not actually intuit a round square. Other kinds of thoughts, though, can have corresponding intuitions. Lacking intuition, we would have no knowledge of existing things at all, only opinions. This is the tradition in which Gödel was thinking of intuition. Later in his career, he would recommend that logicians read Edmund Husserl's (1959-1938) ideas on "categorial intuition," which is a type of rational intuition.

Platonic rationalism, for the logical positivists, was nothing but bad metaphysics.

Gödel was to spend much of his career, however, reacting strongly against empiricist and positivist philosophy. In various places in his writings, he reminded us how his own Platonic rationalism motivated his technical work.

Since, as part of the Vienna Circle, Gödel was situated in the bastion of logical positivism, it may seem obvious why he was so cautious in expressing his philosophical views. And yet, as the logician Solomon Feferman emphasized, neither this experience nor others that were similar influenced him to give up his convictions. To someone with Gödel's delicate mental balance, being surrounded by people with consistently contrary ideas could perhaps even fuel paranoia. It's quite possible that Gödel's extreme caution about expressing his views on Platonism, mathematical intuition, Husserl's phenomenology in later years, and other topics was at least reinforced by his experiences in the Vienna Circle. With Gödel we see the same pattern again and again: he withheld work, worried that he would be attacked or undermined, and out of this caution he failed to respond to certain people or requests. In this way, he resembled another great genius, Isaac Newton.

Social and Academic Developments in the Late Twenties

Around 1928, Gödel first met Adele Porkert Nimbursky (1899–1981) who, 10 years later, would become his wife. She had lived across the street from an apartment Kurt shared with his brother. She had a brief, unhappy marriage to a photographer. Unlike Kurt, she had little formal education and Gödel's parents, especially his father, objected to this relationship. John Dawson, Gödel's biographer, has summed up his parents' objections to Adele: She was a divorcée, a Catholic, came from a lower-class family, had a noticeable facial birthmark, was six years older than Kurt, and was a dancer working at a Viennese nightclub called *Der Nachtfalter*—The Moth. Dancers, at least those who worked in cabarets, were held in ill repute. Although Gödel's father died in 1929, Kurt and Adele did not marry until 1938. As it turned out, they were married for 40 years, until Kurt's death. They had no children, but it was a good marriage. Early on in their life together, Adele had to become a caregiver to Kurt during his periods of physical and mental illness. Many stories, for example, confirm that she was the only one he would trust to prepare his food or to taste it when he became paranoid about being poisoned.

At the time he met Adele, in 1928, Gödel first became seriously interested in mathematical logic. He acquired a copy of Bertrand Russell and Alfred North Whitehead's *Principia Mathematica*. *PM*, as the title is often abbreviated, is a monumental and extremely ambitious multi-volume work in which Russell and Whitehead sought to derive mathematics from a system of axioms of formal logic. This was a program known as "logicism" that had been initiated by the great logician Gottlob Frege, as will be discussed shortly. Two other influences stimulated Gödel's thinking on the subject at around the same time. The first was Carnap's lectures on the philosophical foundations of arithmetic, delivered during the winter semester of 1928-29. Gödel also read the first edition of David Hilbert and Wilhelm Ackermann's book *Principles of Mathematical Logic*, in which both the completeness and decidability of predicate logic were posed as open problems. It was the completeness problem that Gödel solved in his doctoral dissertation. Soon after that, he proved his famous incompleteness theorems in a paper that targets the system of *Principia Mathematica*.

Gödel probably attended a lecture by the brilliant mathematician L.E.J. Brouwer (1881-1966) in March of 1928 in Vienna. Carnap, at any rate, said Gödel was especially influenced by the first of the two lectures, titled *Mathematics, Science, and Language*. Brouwer had originated the program of "intuitionism," which vied with two other programs at the time—logicism and formalism—to put mathematics on a secure foundation. Brouwer's lectures in Vienna were destined to become very influential. They had a significant impact on both Gödel and Wittgenstein. In the introduction to his dissertation, Gödel commented on Brouwer's views, but said later that he did not actually study Brouwer's writings until 1940. It is often reported that Brouwer's first lecture had also stimulated Wittgenstein to return to philosophy. Wittgenstein had to be coaxed into attending the lecture but afterward, in a café, had plenty to say about philosophy.

One other important influence in the late 1920s was Karl Menger. In 1928, he started a mathematics colloquium that Gödel began to attend the following year as his participation in the Vienna Circle waned. In this group, too, he was reticent in non-mathematical discussions but enthusiastic when things got down to the business of logic and mathematics. Gödel attended regularly and participated in many discussions. His contributions were marked by the same characteristics for which he had become known: succinctness, precision, and depth. He published short articles in the colloquium's proceedings and was co-editor of seven of its volumes.

In 1929, Gödel's father died unexpectedly from an abscess of the prostate. Marianne was devastated, becoming more and more lonely and distraught. Kurt and Rudolf junior were alarmed about her health but, otherwise, not much is known about how Kurt reacted to his father's death. The two sons moved Marianne to their apartment in Vienna. All three would go to theater and concerts together, which Kurt enjoyed. It is known that he preferred light opera and Viennese operettas to other music. Rudolf senior, as it turned out, had left his family financially comfortable; Kurt said the family was "close to wealthy" when his father died. Also in 1929, the year Kurt relinquished his Czech citizenship to become an Austrian citizen, he accomplished one of his major intellectual achievements.

In the summer of that year, when he was 23 years old, Gödel solved the completeness problem for what is known as predicate logic. This was in his doctoral thesis, of which he published a revised version in 1930. He received his doctoral degree on Feb. 6, 1930, and presented the results in Menger's colloquium in May. Another presentation followed at what turned out to be a seminal conference in Königsberg in September 1930.

2

The World of Logic

ödel's studies in the late 1920s led him deeper into the world of mathematical logic. A few preliminaries are needed to understand his work in logic and mathematics, including some facts about axiom systems, formalization, formal proof, and the notion of logical truth. These are involved in most of Gödel's work, even to some extent in his later formal "proof" for the existence of God. Although this chapter discusses his completeness theorem, it will not include its mathematical proof. Gödel makes some very interesting claims about how a certain philosophical viewpoint led him to his completeness proof at a time when opposing philosophical viewpoints were preventing other very good logicians from seeing it. He wrote that having the right philosophical outlook—a type of Platonic rationalism or "objectivism"—was an important heuristic in developing his technical work.

Axiom Systems

First, we should consider some key ideas about axiom systems in mathematics and logic. The axiomatic method has been with us for a long time. More than 2,000 years ago, Euclid applied it to the geometry of his day. Since then, axiomatization has been viewed as an ideal way to systematically organize and unify mathematics and logic. Euclid's work has been celebrated, not only in these two fields, but also as an inspiration in literature and poetry, as in Edna St. Vincent Millay's poem, "Euclid alone has looked on beauty bare."

To prove his theorems, Euclid's geometry employed undefined terms, definitions, axioms, rules of inference, and diagrammatic constructions. Beyond geometry, of course, many different areas of mathematics and logic can be axiomatized. The idea, traditionally, has been to start with a specific area or domain such as geometry, the theory of natural numbers, the theory of real numbers, or the theory of sets. Then one lays out as "given" a small number of basic truths that characterize the domain. These are the axioms. Some of the terms used might be primitive, in the sense that no attempt is made to define them. They are taken as intuitively understood. Other terms might then be defined from those primitive expressions. From the small kernel of truths about the domain that the axioms express, the idea is to derive, using valid principles of reasoning, the domain's other truths. The principles of reasoning applied to prove the other truths are the axiom system's primitive rules of inference. The sentences or truths obtained are called the system's theorems. This approach also requires a few basic rules of inference. Little will be gained from an axiom system that contains a large and unwieldy set of axioms and rules of inference. Theorems are derived or proved from the axioms using *only* the rules of inference. One cannot step outside the rules and start using any old pattern of reasoning. Ideally, then, a derivation or proof will show the step-by-step process of obtaining a theorem from the axioms. Once a theorem has been proved, it can be used in proofs of further theorems. Also, as various patterns of reasoning emerge in unfolding the axioms, it is common to formulate new rules of inference derived from the process.

Formal Logic

Logic has a long history in Western philosophy, going back to the ancient Greek philosopher Aristotle, who lived from 384 to 322 B.C.E. Aristotle's work on logic held sway for centuries without significant modifications or extensions. Though logic really started to blossom in the 19th century, one earlier figure is especially important to Gödel's study of logic: this is Gottfried Wilhelm Leibniz, who lived from 1646 to 1716. Leibniz is famous not only as a philosopher. He also, along with Isaac Newton, was one of the inventors of calculus. He had a grand vision for the future of logic. Leibniz wanted to create what he called a "universal characteristic" and a "*calculus ratiocinator.*" By that, he meant an exact universal language, modeled on mathematics, that would express and solve any kinds of problems about which we could reason.

Leibniz himself did not make much headway in actually carrying out this project. It would fall to others to create the universal characteristic and the *calculus ratiocinator*. The great logician Gottlob Frege (1848-1925), deserves most of the credit for bringing at least part of Leibniz's dream to fruition. Frege devised what he called a "concept notation." His plan was to use it in a formal, axiomatic system of logic from which he hoped to derive significant portions of mathematics, starting with arithmetic. He sought to be very rigorous about how axiom systems would work, insisting that proofs contain no gaps, that they not require the use of pictures, diagrams, or intuition as Euclid had, and that all the rules of inference would be laid out in advance so as to circumscribe the reasoning process. This approach would make proofs secure. It would also ensure clarity and avoid the possibility of errors in reasoning. Since Frege thought most of mathematics, except for geometry, could be derived from logical principles alone, his position in the foundations of mathematics is referred to as "logicism." His conception of logic's scope, however, included much more than what today would be regarded as basic logic. Although Frege made tremendous advances, his system of axioms for mathematics has some problems, as we will see below.

Frege's innovations in logical theory were unparalleled. Ironically, however, his own specific notation system was cumbersome and never enjoyed any popularity. His near-contemporary, the mathematician Giuseppe Peano (1858-1932), found a better notation for expressing Frege's innovations in pure formal logic. Without the language of modern logic, it is difficult to understand anything in the field. I will present a few simple examples of some standard formulas and arguments in what is called "predicate logic" or "quantificational logic." This is the logic for which Gödel proved his completeness theorem.

The language of mathematical logic is an artificial language. It is possible to symbolize English sentences or sentences from other natural languages in the language of formal logic. The resulting symbolizations will contain no expressions at all from natural language. The language of logic picks out the *form* or *structure* of our thinking and expression, leaving behind the original content. Nowadays this is comparable to how problems are represented in programming languages, which are also artificial. At the time of Frege and other pioneers in mathematical logic, programming languages did not yet exist, of course. In fact, these early logicians were the ones who laid the foundations for what we now think of as computer science. There are even "descriptive," as distinct from "imperative," programming languages that are based directly on the language of predicate logic. Frege's idea was that the language of logic was to be universal, in the sense that it would pick out the underlying logical structure of expression and thinking, whether in English, Spanish, German, Hindi, Chinese, or other natural languages. Thus, using the language of logic, it is like writing programs in in C^{++} or learning and solving problems in calculus. C^{++} or calculus is the same worldwide, but users of these artificial languages will start from their own natural languages.

Predicate Logic

Learning predicate logic is like learning a new language. We have to get acquainted with the alphabet, the grammar—also called syntax—and the meanings of its expressions. A basic distinction is drawn in modern logic between syntax and semantics. Syntax concerns the forms of the strings of signs that make up the sentences of logic. Those forms are independent of their meanings, or of the sentences' truth or falsity. Semantics, on the other hand, is concerned with precisely these meanings or truth values. In basic logic, semantics addresses the sentences' truth conditions. In Frege's system, the semantics remained informal and not precisely specified. Formal semantics, with its exact definition of truth, did not come into its own until 1935, thanks to the work of Alfred Tarski (1901-1983). Some important semantic concepts will be explored in the section on logical truth in the next chapter.

Consider an expression such as, "If mathematics is fun then mathematics is interesting." Logically speaking, this is a "conditional" sentence. It asserts the idea that mathematics is fun as a condition for its being interesting. In the language of the logic for which Gödel proved his completeness theorem, we can represent the logical "if . . . then . .

. ." function by the symbol "→." We can choose an upper-case Roman letter to stand for the declarative sentence that follows the sentence's "if" part and another upper-case Roman letter to stand for the different sentence that follows the "then" part. For example:

F: "Mathematics is fun."
I: "Mathematics is interesting."

So the symbolization of the English sentence will be "F → I." Note that it would be incorrect to symbolize the sentence as "I → F," because this reverses the dependence relation. Symbolizing sentences in the language of logic is like coding information in a programming language. All the natural language will disappear in favor of the artificial language, just as Leibniz and Frege had wished. We can symbolize declarative sentences in this way whether they are true or false, or even if we do not know which. We are just representing the information's logical form or structure in our artificial language. Several other logical expressions are covered by the basic language of logic. These expressions include "and," "or," "not," "if and only if"—which asserts equivalence—"all," and "some." For example, the sentence "Mathematics is fun and mathematics is interesting" can be symbolized as "F ∧ I," where ∧ stands for "and." Expressions formed with "and" are called *conjunctions*. The expressions "F → I" and "F ∧ I" clearly have different meanings in natural language and the notation reflects this. To take another example, someone might want to say "Mathematics is not fun" or "It is not the case that mathematics is fun." If we use the symbol "¬" for "not" or "it is not the case that," then the symbolization would be "¬ F." Thus "¬" is the symbol for negation. Note that the symbols for logical operators are not completely standardized.

Logicians, mathematicians, and computer scientists are typically quite sensitive to their formal languages' "expressive power." Predicate logic has more expressive power than has been shown so far. Not only can it express relationships between sentences, as in the examples above, but it can also show certain logical relationships that occur within simple sentences. For example, a very basic way of thinking and expressing ourselves involves predication, as when I say, "Raymond is a magician." This sentence asserts that a particular individual, "Raymond," has the property of being a magician, or that he belongs to the set of magicians. The expression "is a magician" is called a "predicate." The sentence is predicating this property of Raymond's. It is typical to use lower-case Roman letters from the first part of the alphabet to symbolize names of individuals, and to use a selected class of upper-case Roman letters to stand for properties or sets. These upper-case letters are the predicates. We can set up a little dictionary to show how we are assigning names to individuals and predicates to properties: let "r" stand for "Raymond" and "M" stand for "is a magician." Then "Mr" is the symbolization of "Raymond is a magician." For "Bill is a logician," we might write "Lb." The grammar of predicate logic typically places the name to the right of the predicate letter. Predicate logic can also express relations between individuals, such as "Andrew loves Mary." Logicians will say "loves" is a two-place predicate. Choosing "a: Andrew" and "m: Mary," we can code the English sentence as "Lam." The relationship would be "Lxy," expressed with the variables "x" and "y." The names take the places held by the variables. Note that the order matters.

That almost concludes our brief explanation of predicate logic. We only need to consider the quantifiers. If I say, "Everything is physical," I have the predicate "is physical" but now also a term that expresses a quantity. This is not saying some particular individual is physical, but that *every* individual is. A standard symbol for "every," "all," or "each" is "(x)". This is called the "universal quantifier." Again, notation for quantifiers is not standardized. The symbolization of "Everything is physical" is "(x)Px." This notation uses the variable "x" in both the quantifier position and in the predicate position to indicate how many individual "x"s are physical.

There is one more quantifier. Instead of saying "Everything is physical," I might want to say, "Something is physical." The symbol combination for "some" is "($\exists$x)" This is called the "existential quantifier." In basic predicate logic, it is understood to mean, "for some x," "there is an x," "there is at least one x," or "there exists an x." So this quantifier asserts that an individual with the property of being physical exists, but it does not pick out any particular individual as a name would. The symbolization, in this case, would be "(∃x) Px." The quantifiers can be combined with other logical operators to form formulas such as "¬ (∃x) Px," which says, "Nothing is physical." Relations with quantifiers can also be expressed. For example, we might have "(∃x)(y)Lxy," which says something "x" stands in the relation "L" to every "y." Assuming that the quantifiers range over the domain of people and that we interpret "Lxy" as defined earlier, this says someone loves everyone.

More than 2,000 years ago, Aristotle already investigated the logic of expressions such as "All men are mortal" and "Some men are mortal" but he had no formal language to express such sentences. In modern predicate logic, "All men are mortal" would be symbolized, with "Mx" for "x is a man" and "Ox" for "x is mortal," as "(x) (Mx → Ox)." The statement "Some men are mortal" would be symbolized as "(∃x) (Mx ∧ Ox)." The expression "(x) (Mx → Ox)" says that for any individual you consider, if it has the property "M," then it also has the property "O." This can also be read as saying that if an individual is in the set "M", then it is also in the set "O." The other expression, "(∃x) (Mx ∧ Ox)," says something has both properties or is in both sets.

To understand Gödel's incompleteness theorems in later chapters, it is important to note that predicate logic's language does not by itself have the stock of symbols needed to represent the axioms of mathematical theories. For example, it does not have in its alphabet the symbol "0," for zero, or a symbol for the successor of a number "s(x)," or "+" and "×" which are needed to express the axioms of arithmetic. In set theory, to take another example, predicate logic lacks the symbol "ε" needed to state that an object is a member of a set. It is often said that, unlike theories in mathematics, logic is topic-neutral. It is not just about natural numbers, or sets, or functions, or other particular kinds of things. Rather, it is about objects of any kind. That means it is natural to distinguish between predicate logic and mathematical theories. Mathematical theories can often be expressed in the language of what is called first-order logic, discussed below, by extending the language with symbols appropriate to the mathematical domain under consideration. Gödel's first incompleteness theorem is an undecidability result that holds for such mathematical theories. Another undecidability result for predicate logic, called Church's theorem, will be discussed briefly below, but this is different from Gödel's completeness theorem for predicate logic. The completeness theorem is about the relationship of logical truth to formal provability. Undecidability, as we will see, is a purely syntactical notion that concerns formal provability. It does not try to relate semantics to syntax.

Arguments, in the sense of logic, are just made up of sentences. The argument's conclusion is a sentence that is supposed to be supported by sentences that provide reasons. Those reasons are called premises. The nature of the "support" is very important. For now, we can say an argument is valid only if its conclusion follows by *necessity* from its premises, and that otherwise, it is not valid. An equivalent way of saying this is that an argument is valid only if it is impossible for its premises to be true while its conclusion is false. We will come back to this in the discussion of semantics below.

The language of predicate logic will allow us to express the forms of many kinds of arguments. As an example, take this argument:

> All cats are animals.
> All animals are mortal.
> Therefore, all cats are mortal.

This can be symbolized as

> $(x) (Cx \rightarrow Ax)$
> $(x) (Ax \rightarrow Mx)$
> Therefore, $(x) (Cx \rightarrow Mx)$

Here we have expressed an argument in what Leibniz had in mind as a portion of a "universal characteristic." As it happens, this is a valid argument. Now could we calculate, using the "*calculus ratiocinator*," whether the argument is valid or not? This was Leibniz's dream. If two people should disagree on an issue, Leibniz hoped they could express their argument symbolically and settle the matter by calculation. "Let us calculate!" he declared. The proof of the conclusion from the premises would be a computation. Everyone will agree on the answer if asked to add a column of figures such as this:

$$7$$
$$3$$
$$2$$
$$\underline{+5}$$
$$?$$

Gödel's completeness theorem applies to predicate logic or quantificational logic. Predicate logic uses quantifiers to express how many individuals we are talking about. The formal language allows us to quantify or express the number of individuals, but does not supply the expressive power to quantify over the properties of those individuals. For example, in predicate logic, we cannot have a formula such as "$(\exists X)(y)\ Xy$," which says there is a property that every individual has. Is there an example of such a property? Yes. Every individual has the property of being identical with itself. Notice how in this formula we have a quantifier for properties and also a quantifier for individuals. In other words, we quantify over predicate places and over expressions for individuals in this formula, while in predicate logic we cannot quantify over predicate places. Now we can be a little bit more precise about Gödel's completeness theorem. It applies to first-order or quantificational logic. In first-order logic, we can quantify over individuals, in second-order logic we can also quantify over properties of individuals, in third-order logic we can also quantify over properties of properties of individuals, and so on. For example, if someone wants to say, "Charles is punctual and punctuality is a virtue" then we can symbolize "Charles is punctual" in first-order logic but not that punctuality has the property of being a virtue. That statement says punctuality—itself a property—has the property of being a virtue, but first-order logic cannot express properties of properties. Thus, "higher-order" logics have more expressive power than first-order logic and can handle more arguments, but they lack some other desirable characteristics. Looking back at Frege, we can note that his "logic" was higher-order logic. First-order logic has many virtues. Few doubt that it's central to elementary logical theory. Gödel proved that first-order logic is complete, which was a substantial achievement. The terrain of logic would look very different had it not been possible to prove this. Likewise, the goal is that everyone should agree on logical properties such as the validity of arguments and the consistency of sets of sentences if we can develop—and then calculate in—Leibniz's "universal characteristic." But is this possible? Can we really hope to solve all problems amenable to reasoning in this way? Does this have limits? Gödel had a lot to say about Leibniz's dream, especially in connection with his incompleteness theorems.

3

The Completeness Theorem

We need to think about a few more points to understand Gödel's main results in logic. First, the idea of axiomatization is very old. Euclid's geometry is presented in axiomatic form. What logicians such as Frege added to this was the creation of a purely formal language in which to express the axioms, definitions, rules of inference and theorems that constitute axiom systems for logic. This would supposedly eliminate the need for diagrams or intuition, and thus remove potential problems with systems such as Euclid's. Frege explicitly cited Leibniz as an inspiration for what he called his "concept notation." Next, we should consider how the famous mathematician David Hilbert (1862-1943) made the idea of "formalization" so exact that it was possible to link formalization with computation. This is a very significant move beyond Euclid and Frege. Hilbert is one of the most important figures in Gödel's story. It was in a book that Hilbert co-wrote with one of his students, Wilhelm Ackermann (1896-1962), that Gödel came upon the problem of proving the completeness of predicate logic. That book was published in 1928. Gödel's incompleteness theorems, as we will see, are also directly related to Hilbert's ideas about the foundations of mathematics.

Strict Formalization

For the moment, we can just look at how Hilbert required formalizations of both logic and mathematics to be exact. First, the *alphabet*—the set of signs—of the formal language to be used must be explicitly specified in advance. Second, we need to explicitly specify in advance how the signs are to be combined to form the language's sentences. This is how the language's "grammar" is laid out. This is done with a small, finite set of rules for constructing the language's "well-formed formulas." These rules, which are now to be given by an algorithm, will tell us what is grammatically—or syntactically—correct in the language and what is not. For example, they would tell us that (x) (Mx → Ox) is well-formed but that (x) Mx → Ox) is not, or that (∃y) Py is well-formed but (∃y) zP is not. Nowadays, this is reflected in computer programming when a program locks up because the programmer has made a "syntax error." That is, a string of symbols in the programming language violates that language's grammar. Third, Hilbert required that all the rules of inference be specified in advance. The set of rules should not be too large. Derived rules can be formulated at later stages in deducing consequences of the axioms.

A "formal proof" of a theorem can then be defined very precisely as a formula obtained by iterated applications of the rules of inference to the axioms or theorems. Each step in the proof is to be justified by citing the axiom, definition, and/or rule of inference used in obtaining the formula at that step. The set of proofs for the system is now defined *algorithmically*, so we are told exactly what falls within the class of proofs. We have a purely formal proof of a formula only when the formula can be derived from the specified axioms or theorems on the basis of the primitive or derived rules of inference.

A purely formal proof, Hilbert said, is just a concrete, finite sequence of formulas obtained only by the rules of inference, where the formulas themselves are concrete, finite configurations of signs formed from the alphabet on the basis of the language's precisely specified rules of grammar. This was brilliant. To operate in an axiom system, in this case, is just to manipulate its syntax according to its rules. Formal provability is a purely "syntactic" notion, which means it does not involve truth, meaning or the references of signs. This is the essence of Hilbert's "formalism." Of course, in axiomatization, as traditionally understood, the intention is to capture the mathematical or logical truths of the domain under investigation. With a purely formal proof, by contrast, it is not necessary to know what is true or false in order to derive theorems from axioms. We abstract away from meaning and truth.

It is also important to note that formal provability is always *relative* to the axioms and rules we have set up. We have different notions of provability if the systems we set up differ from one another in their rules or axioms. This is one of the features that distinguishes actual mathematical practice from working in axiomatic formal systems. To prove theorems in purely formal systems, we need only to be able to recognize the shapes of the signs so that we can operate on them with rules. For example, I can immediately recognize that "The cat is on the mat" and "The cat is on the mat" consist of the same sequence of sign configurations, and that "The cat is on the mat" and "T n□/ rr ti" are different sign configurations. Neither requires that I know anything about the meaning or truth, if any, of those sign configurations. Similarly, in predicate logic, I can see immediately that the sequence of signs $(x)(Px \rightarrow \neg Qx)$ is different from $(x)(\neg Px \rightarrow \neg Qx)$ without having to know anything about the two formulas' meanings or truth conditions.

The notion of an axiomatic formal system can thus be made so exact that generating theorems from axioms, based on the rules of inference, is purely mechanical or algorithmic. A computer could generate the theorems one by one. This does *not* mean that, given an arbitrary formula, the system can decide whether that formula or its negation is a theorem. It means only that the system will keep listing theorems mechanically. The sets of sentences obtainable in this way—the theorems—are said to be computably or recursively enumerable. In the theory of computability, "computably enumerable" sets are distinguished from "computably decidable" or recursive sets. In the case of theorems, a set is computably decidable if a mechanical procedure—an algorithm—exists for deciding whether a given formula or its negation is in the set. This means that if a set A is computably decidable, then A is computably enumerable, but not the other way around. If A is computably decidable then, in fact, both "A" and "not A" are computably enumerable. There are formal theories whose sets of theorems are computably enumerable but not computably decidable. Predicate logic is like this, as the logician Alonzo Church (1903–1995) showed in 1936. This result is known as "Church's theorem."

Turing Machines

A few years after Gödel proved his incompleteness theorems, he came to believe that the logician Alan Turing (1912-1954) had given the definitive theoretical analysis of what computations—that is, mechanical procedures or algorithms—are. Turing defined them in terms of what are now called "Turing machines." His definition of a Turing machine is a mathematically exact characterization of computers. A number of other formal characterizations of mechanical procedures all proved to be equivalent, but Gödel thought Turing's characterization was the clearest, most elementary, and best.

Many functions in mathematics are not algorithmic. Many, also, are algorithmic. What is called "Church's Thesis" is the claim that the intuitive, informal notion of algorithmic function—meaning "mechanical" or "effectively computable"—corresponds to the formal characterizations, that is, to the Turing machine characterization or its equivalents. "CT," as Church's Thesis is often abbreviated, relates the informal notion of algorithm to the exact formal analyses that Turing, Emil Post, Gödel, Church, A.A. Markov, Stephen Kleene, and others gave. It is typically argued that we cannot prove CT because it is not about the relationship of one formal concept to another. Rather, in accepting this thesis—for which the evidence is very good—we are agreeing that any of the equivalent characterizations capture the idea of an algorithmic procedure. This would mean, for example, that if we find a function that is not Turing-machine-computable then we can rest assured that it is not algorithmic. CT was important for someone like Gödel because he was interested in knowing whether there was anything the human mind could do that computers would never be able to do.

Several features of Turing machines should be noted.

1. Since they characterize purely mechanical procedures, they work in a fully determinate, discrete, step-by-step manner that requires no judgment, no imagination, no creativity, and no choice, based on applying an explicit, finite set of rules to finite strings of signs.

2. Also very important is that, as a theoretical concept of mathematics, Turing machines are not taken to be limited by the amount of time or space—for instance, of inputs of 1s and 0s—memory,

or energy available. It is always possible to add more time, space, energy, or memory to a Turing machine computation should any of these be needed by the particular computational task at hand. Actual computers, on the other hand, are always limited by these things. Actual computers are just physical realizations of the mathematical idea of Turing machines.

3. Computable decidability requires that the decision be reached in a finite number of steps or in a finite amount of time, but the size of that finite has no bound or limit. In computability theory, one can go on to characterize the computations' "complexity" as various kinds of bounds on the finite. With actual computers that we use, we know the *full* domain of the finite will always transcend any particular bound that we set. The bounds can be pushed out as we build better and better supercomputers, but actual computers will always have limits.

4. Finally, we are dealing here with precisely specified, formal, *artificial* languages. Sets of sentences of *natural* languages, such as English, Chinese, French or German, are not computably decidable because it cannot be precisely determined which strings count as sentences. What are regarded as "sentences" can vary with time, place, groups of speakers, changes in language, and so on.

Thus, Turing machines are just syntax manipulators that change around strings of bits in a way that is governed by rules. Understanding the idea of strict formalization and its correlation with computation is crucial to Gödel's work in logic and mathematics. Failing to understand that Gödel's work depends on such a rigorous conception of formalization has led to a number of misinterpretations and abuses of his ideas, particularly his incompleteness theorems.

Logical Truth and Semantics

Formal provability is a *syntactic* notion, but in the *semantic* study of logic, truth is the central notion. Modern formal logic is typically divided into its syntactic and semantic sides, each with its distinctive set of notions, syntactic or semantic. Hilbert's emphasis is on syntax. What is called "Hilbert's program," discussed below, is concerned with syntax, not semantics. The development of formal semantics, also called "model theory," came later. As already mentioned, it was Alfred Tarski who launched formal semantics in 1935. In the syntactic study of logic, we define such notions as "well-formed formula," "free and bound variable," "proof," and the like, but we do not consider whether formulas are true or false, nor are we concerned with the logical properties defined by the concept of truth. The semantics of predicate logic, on the other hand, is concerned directly with truth and with logical properties defined in terms of truth. Gödel's completeness theorem is about the relation of syntax to semantics: can all the logical *truths*—a semantic notion—that are expressible in first-order logic be *proved*—a syntactic notion—in a mechanical way from a given axiomatic formal system's axioms and rules of inference? If so, then the system of axioms and rules is said to be *complete*. One could choose different axioms and different rules of inference in different systems, so Gödel's idea is to choose the axioms and rules of inference in such a way as to obtain a complete system. No one before Gödel had proved that a system of first-order or predicate logic was complete.

Truths of logic and mathematics are not like your everyday garden-variety truths. Consider the example of the formula P → (Q → P). When should we count it as true and when false? One can give a rigorous "truth definition" for the various logical operators, including "→," but even before Tarski, it was understood that in predicate logic a sentence of the form "φ → ψ" should be considered false only when "φ" is true and "ψ" is false, and that otherwise it should be considered true. This means that the only way for "P → (Q → P)" to be false would be for "P" to be true and "(Q → P)" to be false. But the only way for "(Q → P)" to be false would be for "Q" to be true and "P" to be false. This, however, is not possible, because we have already said "P" would have to be true for the whole formula to be false. In short, it is *impossible* for "P → (Q → P)" to be false. Here we have exhibited the nature of "logical truth": By definition, a sentence is a logical truth just in case it cannot possibly be false. An equivalent way to say this is that the sentence is not just true but is *necessarily true*. Logical truths are also referred to as "logically valid" sentences. As Leibniz would have said, a sentence that is logically valid is true not only in the actual world but in all possible worlds. Thus, logical truths are different from sentences such as "Barack Obama is president of the United States." This sentence was true when written but is no longer true. Sentences whose truth values can change like this are called "contingent" sentences. They could possibly be true and could also possibly be false. They may be more or less probable, but by definition, they are neither necessary nor impossible. Many of our beliefs, including beliefs in the natural sciences, are contingencies.

It is a simple matter to find formulas in the language of first-order logic that are not logical truths. For example, "Q → P" is not a logical truth because it is possible to assign "Q" the value "T" and "P" the value "F" and then, by the truth definition for "→," the value of "Q → P = F." Because it is not a truth of logic, I should not be able to derive "Q → P" as a theorem from my axioms and rules of inference. We want to be able to capture and prove only the logical truths.

A basic semantic concept involved here is that of an "interpretation." An interpretation in predicate logic consists of specifying a "universe" or domain over which quantifiers range, along with an assignment of referents—individual objects in that universe—to names, if any, and predicates, including relations, in such a way that formulas are evaluated as either true or false. We can interpret the same formula in a variety of ways. For example, for a formula of the propositional fragment of predicate logic such as "Q → P" we have the following interpretations: let "Q = T" and "P = T," or "Q = T" and "P = F," or "Q = F" and "P = T," or both can be false. Thus, another way to characterize logically valid sentences is to say they are true under all interpretations.

Another basic semantic concept is that of a "model." A model of a formula or set of formulas is an interpretation that makes that formula, or every formula in the set, true. Logicians are often interested in determining whether sets of formulas, such as sets of axioms, have models. In Gödel's deep work in set theory, for example, he found an interesting model for a standard set of axioms in this area of mathematics.

In axiomatic formal logic, viewed not merely syntactically but in terms of the semantic notion of truth, the axioms should all be logically valid and so should all the theorems derived from those axioms. This means the rules of inference should take us from logically valid sentences to logically valid sentences. We should never be able to obtain from the rules of inference a sentence that is not logically valid. If we input logical truths, which is what the axioms should be, into the system, then it should mechanically output only logical truths.

The Completeness Theorem

The terminology of Gödel's completeness and incompleteness theorems is potentially misleading. Unfortunately, the term "completeness" is used differently in the completeness theorem from how it is used in the incompleteness theorems. In the sense of the completeness theorem, "completeness" relates semantics to syntax. It means the axioms and rules of inference used in a system of predicate logic are sufficient to prove every logically valid formula. But in the sense of the incompleteness theorems, the word "completeness" would be better replaced by the term "decidability," which is a purely syntactical notion. "Completeness" in this sense means that for any formula "φ" of an axiomatic formal theory the theory proves either "φ" or "$\neg \varphi$." It means we have a "decision procedure"; that is, we have computable decidability.

We can work *inside* an axiomatic formal system, proving more and more theorems, as when we prove more and more theorems of predicate logic. There are some very important properties, however, that we would like axiomatic formal systems as a whole to have. We can think of these systems as theoretical computers, that is, Turing machines. With strict formalization, we can make the axiomatic formal system itself the object of our thinking. It is an exactly specified object. Here we are looking at the system from the *outside*. We want to know certain things about it as a whole. A very important property of any axiomatic formal system is that it should be *consistent*. A simple way to define this, involving the notion of truth, is to say that an axiomatic formal system of logic is consistent if it proves only logical truths, that is, logically valid sentences. Consistency in this semantic sense is often called "soundness." It is also possible to give a purely syntactical definition of "consistency" that does not use the notion of truth. Gödel does this as part of his incompleteness theorems.

It is a big problem if a system is not consistent because

inconsistency undermines the point of the system. If we can derive an inconsistency in a mathematical system, then that system as a whole is worthless. "Inconsistency" is just another word for "contradiction." In classical logic, any sentence can be derived from a contradiction. This can be seen by considering the semantic definitions of "contradiction" and "validity." A sentence is a contradiction just in case it is necessarily false, or is false under every interpretation. An argument is valid just in case it is impossible for all its premises to be true but its conclusion to be false. Alternatively, the argument is valid if no possible interpretation would make all its premises true but its conclusion false. Now consider any argument that has a contradiction in its premises. In this case, it is impossible for all the premises to be true, because one of those premises is a contradiction. Hence, any such argument is by definition automatically valid, which trivializes our reasoning. Any formula at all will validly follow from a contradiction. In mathematics, this is intolerable. It is why we want to avoid inconsistency at all costs. We could never get started in any field of inquiry. We will see a famous example of an inconsistent axiomatic system in a later chapter.

We would not necessarily need to abandon a whole system if a contradiction can be derived in it. Sometimes it is possible to patch up the system by finding the source of the contradiction. Then that contradictory source can be swapped out for a modified axiom or rule of inference that does not, or is not known to, generate a contradiction. Also, we do not always know whether axiomatic formal systems are consistent. This may be unknown one way or the other for many years, perhaps indefinitely. We will see examples in later chapters of systems for which it is now unknown whether they are consistent. Because axiomatic formal systems are exact, we can ask for rigorous mathematical proofs that they are consistent. So these are mathematical proofs about the systems as a whole.

Another very desirable property of axiomatic formal systems—the property on which Gödel focused—is that they should be *complete*. A simple way to define this semantically—that is, in terms of the notion of truth—is to say that an axiomatic formal system of logic is *complete if it proves all of the logical truths, that is, all of the logically valid sentences*. Axiomatic formal systems may possess or lack other important properties, such as categoricity, but we will not go into these here. Also, one can set up the axioms and rules of inference for first-order logic in different ways. The system for which Gödel proved his completeness theorem is the first-order part of the system given in Russell and Whitehead's *Principia Mathematica*. As Gödel noted, this system is similar to the one given in the Hilbert and Ackermann book of 1928.

With this background, we can now state Gödel's completeness theorem very simply.

Gödel's Completeness Theorem: All logically valid sentences of first-order (or predicate) logic are provable.

Remember that "provable" here means *formally provable* in a mechanical way. Thus, one reason this theorem is important is that it shows that, in principle, Leibniz's dream of a universal language of logic can be at least partially realized. We do not have computable decidability, but we do have computable enumerability of the theorems that, by completeness, are also the logical truths. In this case, we have captured the truths of predicate logic in an axiomatic formal system.

To appreciate Gödel's achievement, think of what would be required to prove rigorously that *all* valid formulas are provable. We cannot just go through every formula one by one to verify this. There are too many. In principle, there is a "denumerable infinity" of formulas. (Chapter 8 includes the definition of "denumerability.") Instead of testing formulas one at a time, one has to use mathematics that is more advanced. While we are not considering the proof of the completeness theorem in detail here, it would be intellectually rewarding for the reader to study it in more depth. In his completeness paper, Gödel also established some other results about first-order logic. The interested reader might investigate these independently.

Gödel said that since the axioms of the system under consideration are valid and the rules of inference are correct in that they preserve truth, it is clear that if a formula is provable, then it is valid. In other words, the system is sound. By the completeness theorem we also know the converse: if a formula is valid, then it is provable. This means that for predicate logic, formal provability and logical validity—logical truth—turn out to be equivalent in extension: all logical truths, and only the logical truths, are provable. The system will suffice to prove all and only the logical truths formally. In this context, it is not as though the human mind has some grasp of truth that would transcend the capabilities of a computer (a Turing machine) to output that truth. We do not have computable decidability here, but we still have a significant result.

Gödel's Philosophy and the Completeness Theorem

On various occasions, Gödel made comments about the role his philosophical views played in his technical work in mathematical logic. In 1967, when Hao Wang questioned him about his completeness theorem, Gödel argued that other logicians at the time had failed to prove the completeness theorem because they lacked "the required epistemological attitude toward metamathematics and toward non-finitary reasoning." One of these logicians, who made a deep contribution to other parts of the subject, was the Norwegian Thoralf Skolem (1887-1963). He had come very close to proving the theorem. Gödel said Skolem and others had been held back by a restricted philosophical view that rejected all kinds of abstract or infinitary objects, including the meanings of mathematical symbols. Gödel said this blindness among logicians was surprising, and that it was rooted in a philosophical prejudice. Since completeness is concerned with the sufficiency of formal deductions, it might seem that it need not appeal to abstract or infinitary objects, meanings, or truths. Completeness, however, requires a connection with the concept of logical validity: that is, with necessary *truths*. So the proof was missed, even though the mathematical components needed for it were available. Gödel said one of the prejudices among logicians at the time was that they viewed the concept of truth with great suspicion, widely regarding it as meaningless.

Gödel described his own view, by contrast, as "objectivistic." This is Gödel's Platonic rationalism, which is the view that abstract, infinitary, and mind-independent objects and truths exist in mathematics and logic, and that we can know about them based on our capacity for reason or rational intuition. Gödel said this Platonistic point of view also played an important role in finding his incompleteness theorems and his consistency results in set theory. This will be discussed in later chapters.

It was only after doing all of the work on the completeness theorem on his own that Gödel presented it to his doctoral thesis advisor, Hans Hahn. He then began to think through ideas that would lead to the incompleteness theorems.

4

Background to the Incompleteness Theorems

S ome scholars say 1930 was the most important year of Gödel's life because that was when he wrote his famous incompleteness paper. We know from Carnap's diary that already on Dec. 23, 1929, in a discussion in the *Arkadencafe* in Vienna, Gödel had spoken about the "inexhaustibility of mathematics." As a consequence of this inexhaustibility, he said, one must always draw afresh from the "fountain of intuition." Carnap noted that Gödel was prompted to say this by Brouwer's March 1928 lecture in Vienna. On that occasion, Gödel said mathematics is not completely formalizable, and that there is no universal characteristic and no decision procedure for the whole of mathematics. All these points would remain part of his view of the incompleteness theorems. In his so-called "Gibbs lecture" of 1951, which addressed the philosophical implications of the incompleteness theorems, he again used this expression "the inexhaustibility of mathematics."

A number of important developments led up to the incompleteness theorems. We should briefly review these to grasp the significance of Gödel's work.

Historical Background to the Incompleteness Theorems

Gödel's incompleteness theorems emerged against the background of reactions to a foundational "crisis" in mathematics. This was brought on by the discovery of paradoxes in Georg Cantor's (1845-1918) set theory and in Gottlob Frege's efforts to derive mathematics—all except geometry—from basic axioms of his very broad conception of "logic."

For Frege, logic was not just first-order logic; it was higher-order logic. One of Frege's axioms, which he called "Basic Law V," was shown by Bertrand Russell to lead to a paradox. One could literally derive a contradiction from it. The paradox came to be known as "Russell's paradox." Paradoxes had also been detected in Cantor's set theory, some by Cantor himself.

Russell's paradox, and others that affected set theory, led to a crisis in the foundations of mathematics. Why? Pure mathematics typically has been thought of as the most rigorous, secure, and certain of the sciences. If anything is reliable, pure mathematics should be. It had traditionally been considered to be the domain of necessary, *a priori* truths. How could something like this happen? How could it be prevented from ever happening again? In operating with this axiom system, mathematicians were actually operating under an illusion.

The paradoxes led to a host of reactions. One was to modify the axiom or law that led to the paradox, restricting it in some way, but without completely abandoning the theory of sets that Cantor had devised or the theory of extensions of concepts that Frege had developed. This is the path that Ernst Zermelo (1871-1953) took, as described in Chapter 8 on set theory. Russell himself reacted differently, by putting forward his theory of types, which would not allow paradoxical expressions to be formed in the language of the theory. Other reactions called for a more extensive reworking of the foundations of mathematics. The reaction most important for understanding Gödel's incompleteness theorems was put forward by Hilbert. This is known as "Hilbert's program," "formalism," or "proof theory," and depends on what Hilbert called "metamathematics."

Hilbert's Program

Hilbert was a wide-ranging mathematician. He contributed remarkable results in many areas, including mathematical physics, for which he is justly famous. Hilbert was deeply disturbed by the foundational crisis, and he set forth a program that he thought would put mathematics on a reliable foundation once and for all.

His idea was to start by axiomatizing and strictly formalizing areas of mathematics, as described above. In particular, this should be done for Cantorian set theory (see Chapter 8) since its scope is so broad that virtually all of mathematics can be derived from it, and because it was the site of most of the paradoxes. In setting up his program, Hilbert said, "No one shall be able to drive us from the paradise that Cantor created for us." Hilbert wanted to save Cantorian set theory by putting it on a firm foundation. Axiomatized and strictly formalized parts of mathematics, even though highly regimented, are still parts of mathematics. What Hilbert called "metamathematics" takes these formal systems as its object. Metamathematics studies their properties as syntactical systems, in particular, to determine whether they are consistent and complete. Consistency is especially important in ensuring that we will never again be deceived by contradictions. What this means in syntactical terms is this: we want to prove mathematically that for the axiomatic formal theory in question, we can never derive a sign configuration having the form "A" and also a sign configuration having the form "¬A." For completeness, for every formula "A" in the system, we should be able to derive either "A" or "¬A." That is, we should be able to prove that the formulas in the system are computably decidable.

In 1926, Hilbert described the philosophical foundation of his view in a very striking way:

> as a condition for the use of logical inferences and the performance of logical operations something must already be given to our faculty of representation, certain extralogical concrete objects that are intuitively present as immediate experience prior to all thought. If logical inference is to be reliable it must be possible to survey these objects completely in all their parts, and the fact that they occur, that they differ from one another, and that they follow each other, or are concatenated, is immediately intuitively given, together with the objects, as something that neither can be reduced to anything else nor requires reduction. This is the basic philosophical position that I consider requisite for mathematics and, in general, for all scientific thinking, understanding, and communication. And in mathematics, in particular, what we consider is the concrete signs

themselves, whose shape, according to the conception we have adopted, is immediately clear and recognizable.

A formula in an axiomatic formal system is just a finite, concrete sign configuration that—in principle—is immediately given in sense perception. If we think of formulas as finite sequences of signs drawn from our alphabet, then proofs are finite sequences of these finite sequences. A proof, in other words, is also just a finite, concrete sign configuration that, in principle, is immediately given in sense perception. Here Hilbert invokes some ideas of the famous philosopher Immanuel Kant, whose notion of intuition is restricted to sensory intuition and to what he calls its two forms, space and time. Concrete signs are given in space and time. Moreover, as we have already seen, formalism in Hilbert's sense abstracts away from the signs' meanings. We should never have to consider the meanings or references of the sign configurations. We should only calculate with the sign configurations, outputting particular sign configurations from given sign configurations on the basis of the specified rules of inference. This is just what computers do.

Hilbert contrasted the finite with the infinite, the concrete with the abstract, the immediately given in sensory intuition, which is "prior to all thought," with what is part of pure thought, and meaningless sign configurations with the meanings of sign configurations. In some of his writings, he said his foundational viewpoint keeps us in the sphere of the "real," not the ideal. We can point out that since Hilbert's meaningless sign configurations are given in space and time, they are objects with which we interact on a cause-and-effect basis. All these features, he thought, should take the mystery out of mathematics that led to the contradictions in set theory.

The position in the philosophy of mathematics that Gödel embraced—Platonic rationalism—adopts just those notions that are on the other side of the distinctions on which Hilbert depended. As a Platonist, Gödel thought we could cautiously accept the existence of at least certain forms of the infinite. He also accepted abstract objects that are not given immediately in sense perception, in space and time, or in the cause-and-effect nexus. In various writings, for example, Gödel spoke of the abstract *meanings* of symbols as such objects. We know about some objects on the basis of reason or rational intuition. The rationalist says not all knowledge has to be based on sense experience. For many rationalists, sense experience is, in fact, a defective source of knowledge. Because axiomatic formal systems, described in work after Hilbert, can be viewed in terms of Turing machines, Gödel also put forward some views on the differences between human minds and computers.

Hilbert's program has another crucial component. The idea is to prove that axiomatic formal systems (that is, computers) are syntactically consistent. The whole project would be pointless, however, if we could help ourselves to any mathematics we like to obtain such a proof. So the other important component is that the mathematics we use to prove the consistency of such systems as higher set theory must itself be finitary and concrete. This is Hilbert's "finitism."

Several axiomatic formal systems figure into a lot of Gödel's work, and it will be a good idea to note them now with their usual abbreviations. The axiomatic formal system of arithmetic, formalized by Giuseppe Peano, is known as Peano arithmetic or "PA." This is a first-order formalization. The extensive system of Russell and Whitehead, *Principia Mathematica*, or "PM," is not a first-order formalization. The system of set theory called Zermelo-Fraenkel set theory, "ZF," is a first-order formalization. An extension of ZF that includes an additional axiom, the axiom of choice, is referred to as "ZFC," which is also a first-order theory. These standard abbreviations, PA, PM, ZF, and ZFC, will be used throughout the remainder of this book. It is not necessary to know in detail what these axiomatic formal systems are. Relevant points about them will emerge as we proceed.

Proving the Incompleteness Theorems: Key Ideas

After completing his doctoral thesis, Gödel began to work on proving the consistency of the theory of real numbers, following the Hilbert program. He came to realize that truth in arithmetic could not be defined in arithmetic without landing in the Liar Paradox, to be discussed below. Formal provability in arithmetic, however, could be defined in arithmetic. This meant that if the provable formulas of arithmetic are all true, then there must be some true but unprovable arithmetic formulas. Working out all of this, with his original plan of contributing to the Hilbert program, is what led to the incompleteness theorems. It was while working on the Hilbert program that Gödel was led to results—the incompleteness theorems—that put an end to Hilbert's program in its original form!

Following a mathematical proof of the incompleteness theorems requires advanced training in logic. Instead of presenting the mathematical proof, I will just describe key ideas that go into the proofs. In a number of these ideas, we see Gödel's genius at work.

Stated in its general form, the first incompleteness theorem can be put as follows:

Gödel's First Incompleteness Theorem: If an axiomatic formal system of mathematics containing arithmetic is consistent, then it is incomplete.

We should immediately comment on the meaning of this theorem to indicate what it says clearly. This statement of the first theorem is not exactly what Gödel proved in his famous paper. It is instead a more general version that depends on the work in 1936 of the logician J. Barkley Rosser (1907–1989). Second, both incompleteness theorems have very general application. Perhaps the best way to see this is to realize that the very powerful part of mathematics from which basically all of mathematics can be derived—set theory—contains arithmetic, and the incompleteness theorems apply to set theory. Third, technically speaking there are axiomatic formal systems for very minimal parts of mathematics, such as arithmetic with "+" but without "×" (called "Presburger arithmetic"), to which the incompleteness theorems do not apply. This happens because the systems do not contain enough arithmetic to allow Gödel numbering. From the point of view of ordinary mathematical practice, however, a system such as this is contrived. There are all sorts of truths of arithmetic we could not prove in Presburger arithmetic.

The first theorem, in particular, says that if it is impossible to prove both P and $\neg P$ in an axiomatic formal system of mathematics, then the system will have a formula, call it G, such that neither G nor $\neg G$ will be provable in the system. In other words, G is *undecidable* in the system if the system is consistent. This very formula G is true, however, if the system is consistent. So here will be at least one mathematical truth that is not provable in the system in question if that system is consistent.

It is often said that the first incompleteness theorem tells us that mathematical truth is not equal to formal proof. Formal proof is arithmetic in nature, but truth is not. It is also worth keeping in mind that axiomatic formal systems are Turing machines, so we are speaking of the limitations on computers that can do some arithmetic. Such computers cannot be both consistent and complete.

Gödel's Second Incompleteness Theorem: If an axiomatic formal system of mathematics containing arithmetic is consistent, then it is impossible to prove the system's consistency using the mathematics available in the system.

This theorem is especially deleterious to Hilbert's program. This is because Hilbert wanted to prove stronger systems such as ZF set theory that were consistent using a relatively weak system of finitist mathematics. According to the second incompleteness theorem, however, strong systems are necessary to prove the consistency of weak systems, a complete reversal of Hilbert's idea! Now think of what this means in the context of the philosophical ideas discussed above that were supposed to undergird the Hilbert program. Those ideas were about the concrete, the finitary, meaning, causality, and what is given in spatio-temporal intuition. We will discuss the implications of the incompleteness theorems in Chapter 6.

It is important to note that Gödel proved the incompleteness theorems in a form that would be acceptable to any of the schools in the foundations of mathematics. The theorems apply even if we regard sentences of a formal system as mere sequences of symbols, irrespective of their truth or falsity or of any meaning they may have. According to some foundational views, for example, the sentences of higher set theory such as ZFC are not meaningful or do not express truths. Yet these same foundational views will still recognize that the incompleteness theorems apply to higher set theory because the theorems are concerned with manipulation of finitary syntax. On the basis of the incompleteness theorems, it is not necessary to believe that the sentences of higher mathematics are true. The theorems do tell us, however, that *if* the systems are syntactically consistent, then the Gödel sentences for those systems are true.

5

Proving the Incompleteness Theorems

How are the incompleteness theorems proved? For the first theorem, we need to find an undecidable formula G that is nonetheless true if the system is syntactically consistent. There are several elements of the proof that should be discussed.

(1) *Gödel numbering*, (2) What G is, and (3) The clever reasoning that shows us that G is undecidable but nonetheless true if we are working in a consistent system. We can start with the brilliant idea of "Gödel numbering."

Gödel Numbering

In his discussions of the universal characteristic and *calculus ratiocinator,* Leibniz thought of our concepts as having unique numbers associated with them, so operating logically with concepts just amounts to calculating with these numbers. We need to determine the numbers of our concepts to carry out Leibniz's plan for logic. Leibniz, by the way, was very fond of binary arithmetic, in which all calculations are performed with only the numbers 1 and 0, as in modern digital computers.

These ideas were remarkably insightful because we now know, thanks to Gödel's work, that we can assign a unique number to each sentence in an axiomatic formal system. In Turing's case, we can assign a number to each particular set of instructions that characterizes a Turing machine. Nowadays this is a common idea in theoretical computer science. While it is true that we express concepts in language, however, it would be a very tall order to determine the unique numbers associated with each of our *concepts* unless, implausibly, concepts themselves are reducible to meaningless pieces of syntax. In Gödel numbering, numbers are assigned to strings of syntax, that is, to concrete, finite sign configurations that need not even be interpreted. Gödel numbering is not the same thing as assigning numbers to *abstract* meanings that, according to Platonism, interpreted formulas are supposed to express. Operating with meanings, as distinct from concrete sign configurations, would make a huge difference between human minds and machines.

We should note that what computers and formal systems compute with are numerals, not numbers. There are many different numeral systems that can be used to express the same number in concrete symbols. For example, the number 4 can be expressed in Roman numerals as IV, in strings of strokes as IIII, or in different ways in Chinese, Mayan, Egyptian hieroglyphic, Attic Greek, Babylonian, or other numeration systems. Four can also be expressed in a base 2 numeration system as 100, and in many other bases. In PA the number 4 is expressed as ssss0. We cannot identify the number with any of these concrete numerals, and yet all of these numerals express the same number. We cannot actually write down the number.

Let us now consider a simple example of how Gödel numbering works. There are many ways to set up systems of Gödel numbering. To indicate how it works, I will present only a partial illustration, enough to show how to encode one of the axioms of a formal system of arithmetic. (This is a toy coding system, different from the one that Gödel originally used.) The language of formal arithmetic requires several of its own special symbols, such as 0, s, =, +, and the notion of a number's successor, which is what the symbol *s* stands for, figures into several of the axioms of arithmetic. The successor of a number is just the next number that follows in the ordinary sequence of natural numbers. Thus, 2 is the successor of 1, 3 is the successor of 2, and so on. In axiomatic formal arithmetic, however, numbers are denoted by using the successor function s(x). Thus, s0 is the standard expression for 1, ss0 is the expression for 2, and so on. Now one of the usual axioms of arithmetic says that if two numbers have the same successor, then they are the same number. In other words, no two numbers have the same immediate successor. In the notation of formal arithmetic, the axiom is

$(x)(x')((s(x) = s(x')) \rightarrow (x = x'))$.

To code this formula in a system of Gödel numbering, we only need to be able to use the coding system on the string of signs. This is just like coding words or instructions in strings of 1s and 0s in Turing machines.

Let us specify our toy system of Gödel numbering as follows:

Symbol	Gödel number (gn)	Symbol meaning
¬	1	not
→	2	if . . . then
x	3	individual variable
=	4	equals
0	5	zero
s	6	the successor of
(	7	parenthesis, for grouping
)	8	parenthesis, for grouping
'	9	prime, used to distinguish a variable from another variable, for example, x from x'

Using this coding scheme, we can write down the gn of our axiom of arithmetic. It is

7387398776738467398827343988

Thus, we can look at the axiom $(x)(x')((s(x) = s(x')) \rightarrow (x = x'))$ as 7387398776738467398827343988 or vice versa. With a properly constructed and full system of Gödel numbering, we can encode as numbers all the axioms and theorems in our axiomatic formal system of arithmetic. A unique gn can be assigned to every formula. In the other direction, given a number, we can determine whether it is the gn of a formula and, if so, retrieve the formula. This can all be done algorithmically.

In axiomatic formal arithmetic itself, we want to prove various arithmetic truths, such as the commutative property of addition, which says that x + x′ = x′ + x for all x and x′. In the notation of Peano arithmetic,

$$(x)(x')\ (x + x' = x' + x).$$

With Gödel numbering, however, we can code all the formulas of formal systems as numbers. Since proofs are just finite sequences of formulas in which a formula is derived from another formula or formulas, we can also code the proofs. In the case of a proof, the proof's premises will have a gn and so will the conclusion, that is, the theorem derived from the premises.

Expressions of syntactic concepts, such as "axiom," "formula," "proof," "theorem," and the like, do not occur in formal axiomatic arithmetic; but now the metamathematical statement that there is a proof of a formula can just as well be understood as saying that a particular *number*—the gn of the premises—stands in a particular *arithmetical* relation to the *number* of the conclusion. From the axiom above, for example, we can prove in arithmetic an instance of the axiom, such as s(0) = s(0) → 0 = 0. The gn of this latter formula is 6758467582545. Gödel's proof shows, in effect, that some purely arithmetical relation holds between this number and the number of the axiom, 7387398776738467398827343988, if and only if the instance can be proved from the axiom. Statements *about* the system, such as the statement that a formula is provable from some other formulas, can now be expressed *within* the system as an arithmetic relation between certain numbers. The system in this case, after all, is a formalization of arithmetic itself. The *outside* can be brought *inside*. In this manner, we can completely "arithmetize metamathematics." What we call a *formula* of the system can be seen as a number; various relations between formulas can now be seen as arithmetic relations between numbers; and so on.

Now let us ask what we are saying when we assert that there is no proof of a formula. This means, by way of the Gödel numbering, that no gn (of premises) stands in the appropriate arithmetical (proof) relation to the gn of the formula to be proved. We can think of this as just adding a negation sign to the front of the metamathematical expression that a formula has a proof.

The Gödel Sentence G and Reasoning Leading to the Incompleteness Theorems

What Gödel did is to show how to construct a sentence in any of the given mathematical systems that in effect says of itself, metamathematically speaking, that it is not provable in the system. If it is PM that we are considering, then we will be able to construct a statement that says of itself that it is not provable in PM. To be a little more precise, he constructs in a system S a statement G that says no natural number x is the gn of a proof in S of a certain formula A, but A happens to be G itself. Thus, G says, in effect, "This sentence is unprovable (in S)." We can obtain a kind of self-reference. G is the sentence I have called the Gödel sentence for the system. Let us call it G_s to indicate that it is the Gödel sentence for the mathematical system S that we pick. As we said, S could be the formal system of arithmetic PA, or it could be PM, or ZF set theory, and so on. Thus, we could have G_{PA}, G_{PM}, and so on. I will not try to show technical details of how Gödel constructed this sentence. It is done by using an important technique called "diagonalization."

Gödel mentioned that G is analogous to what we find in the Richard Paradox or in the ancient paradox of the Liar. Let us consider the Liar Paradox since it is simpler. In the Liar Paradox, we have a sentence that asserts its own falsity. The Liar sentence says, "This sentence is false." When we suppose the Liar sentence is true, we find that, on account of what it says, it must be false. On the other hand, when we suppose it is false, we find that, on account of what it says, it must be true. Either way, we have a contradiction. In that paradox, Gödel saw that truth in arithmetic cannot be expressed or defined in arithmetic without landing in a contradiction. He also saw that if we substitute "unprovable" for "false", we get G, except that now, thanks to the arithmetization of metamathematics, G is expressible in the system. Moreover, we do not get a contradiction, but rather we get the undecidability of G if the system is consistent!

Hence, the reasoning for undecidability is as follows. If G_S ("This sentence is unprovable (in S)") were provable, then its formal negation, whose interpretation is "This sentence is provable (in S)" would also be provable, which is a contradiction. Similarly, if $\neg G_S$ were provable, then G_S would be provable, which is also a contradiction. On the assumption that S is consistent, however, neither G_S nor $\neg G_S$ can be provable. If S is consistent, then G_S is formally undecidable. On account of what G_S says, however, it must be *true*. It says, "This sentence is unprovable (in S)" and so it asserts the truth. Moreover, by the Gödel numbering and some facts about it, we know this is an arithmetical truth.

It is important to note that this undecidability is only with respect to provability *inside* S. From the *outside* it is clear that G_S is true. In other words, G_S is undecidable in S if S is consistent; but Gödel's proof shows by metamathematical reasoning that G_S is true. There are statements that, viewed from the *outside* of such systems, can be seen to be true if the system is consistent, but they cannot be proved *inside* the systems. So we now have an arithmetic formula, by way of the Gödel numbering, such that neither it nor its negation is provable in a system S if S is consistent. This was just how we stated the first incompleteness theorem above. A formal theory in which a sentence is undecidable is incomplete:

> If an axiomatic formal system of mathematics containing arithmetic is consistent then it is incomplete.

One might think that since the undecidability of G_S is only undecidability with respect to S, and since G_S is true, we could just add G_S to S as an axiom, obtaining a new system S_1. In S_1, G_S would no longer be undecidable since it is now a formula of S_1. Gödel's proof, however, shows that there would be a new Gödel sentence G_{S1} for S_1 that would be undecidable if S_1 is consistent. This pattern just repeats. We can keep constructing Gödel sentences for these new systems S_1, S_2, S_3, S_4, . . . and we will never get a complete system. In this sense, we will not be able to provide *finite axiomatizations* of mathematics with these formal systems if they are consistent. As a Platonic rationalist might put it, we uncover more and more arithmetic truths. These truths transcend the axiomatic formal system at each stage. The Platonist would hold that truth is independent of the finite, concrete axiomatic systems or machines and that more truths are, as it were, waiting to be discovered. We can keep ascending on the basis of reason to more truths, but we will always fall short of grasping them all.

In 1938, Alan Turing published an interesting paper called "Systems of Ordinal Logics." In it, he investigated whether it was possible to overcome incompleteness if we consider systems that we extend beyond the finite ordinals that we index with 1, 2, 3, . . . to transfinite constructive ordinals such as ω, $\omega + 1$, . . . $\omega + \omega$, and so on (see Chapter 8 on set theory). This means we would be considering systems such as S_ω, $S_{\omega + \omega}$, and so on. The answer is "no" but some other interesting facts do turn up along the way, and Turing is led to the claim that we must use intuition and ingenuity in these ordinal logics.

It is also interesting to pause over Gödel's insight that truth in arithmetic cannot be expressed or defined in arithmetic without landing in a contradiction. As the logician Alfred Tarski put it in 1936, to define truth for arithmetic we have to ascend to a "higher" level language. This leads to what is called "Tarski's indefinability theorem." If L is the formal language of arithmetic, then to avoid the Liar Paradox we must extend L to a new language L'. This gives us the means to refer to expressions of L and contains the predicates "true in L" and "false in L." Such "truth predicates" are always superscripted to language level. To express truth or falsity for L, we have to go to L'; to express truth or falsity for L' we have to go to the next level, L'', and so on. We thus get a Tarskian hierarchy of ever-increasing, richer languages. Thus, we cannot get the Liar Paradox started because truth for a given level is always expressed by a predicate of the next level. The Liar sentence would now be viewed as always relative to language level. It says, for example, "This sentence is false in L." We cannot go on to ask whether the sentence is true or false in L, which would generate the paradox, because the sentence is already in L' and so could not be true or false in L. The sentence is simply false instead of paradoxical. Gödel would have no trouble with this and already saw the basic point before Tarski, but he remarked about how he used a "highly transfinite concept of objective mathematical truth" as a heuristic to obtain his incompleteness results. Here he was thinking outside the box of pure formalism and logical positivism. He was using his Platonic rationalism. As the logician and computer scientist Martin Davis has put it, Gödel was thinking thoughts that were strictly forbidden by the Vienna Circle because, for them, any notion of mathematical truth other than formal provability was supposed to be meaningless.

The second incompleteness theorem is proved in the following way. We know from the first theorem that G_s is true but unprovable in S if S is consistent. Although G_s cannot be proved in S, what can be proved in S is the formula expressing the conditional statement

(*) If S is consistent then G_s.

Now we can reason this way: "S is consistent" is not provable in S, for if it were, then by (*), G_s would be provable. We have already seen that unless S is inconsistent, G_s is not provable in S. Therefore, if S is consistent, then the formula expressing "S is consistent" is not provable in S. This is Gödel's second incompleteness theorem.

It does not follow from the second incompleteness theorem that there could be no consistency proofs for any of the systems S to which the theorem applies, but we do know that such consistency proofs would require mathematics not formalized in S. They would require, generally speaking, more powerful mathematics. For example, the logician Gerhard Gentzen (1909-1945) proved that arithmetic is consistent using a type of *transfinite* reasoning. In later work, in his so-called "Dialectica" paper, Gödel also showed that arithmetic is consistent if we allow ourselves to reason with some mathematical ideas that are stronger than what is available in arithmetic. Gödel and others went on to explore the philosophical consequences of this situation, as we will see below. We can already determine, however, that Hilbert's original program will not work. The second incompleteness theorem, in particular, tells us that we will not be able to have a *finitist* consistency proof for axiomatic formal systems of mathematics because, whatever finitist mathematics F is, it will not even suffice to prove the consistency of F. All the features of finitist reasoning that were supposedly so desirable are, in effect, undermined by the second theorem. The second theorem, as we said, actually reverses the situation that Hilbert desired. Instead of showing that axiomatic formalizations of strong parts of mathematics could be proved consistent using only finitist, concrete mathematics, one has to use stronger parts of mathematics to show that the formalizations of weaker parts are consistent. In effect, one has to use abstract concepts to prove that concrete mathematics is consistent; one has to use infinitary concepts to prove that finitist mathematics is consistent; and so on.

The more Gödel pondered this situation, the more he became concerned about how to develop a version of Platonic rationalism that could avoid the problems with earlier forms of Platonic metaphysics and rationalist epistemology. This is not something for which the philosophical ideas of the Vienna Circle would have prepared him. Quite the contrary. It was in the philosophical writings of Plato, Leibniz and eventually Husserl that Gödel thought he might find a defensible form of Platonic rationalism. With his very high standards of rigor, though not necessarily always formal rigor, he hoped that it would eventually be proved that a form of Platonic rationalism provided the correct conception of logic and mathematics. I think this is one of the reasons why he never published his critique of Carnap's idea that mathematics is syntax of language. He believed in a form of Platonic rationalism and had, according to his own words, used it to obtain his most important logical results. But he could not come close to proving Platonic rationalism and would not publish a critique that was likely to be attacked because it did not offer a rigorously convincing alternative to Carnap's view. In his remarks to Wang, in particular, he was pointing out where we might look to obtain such a rigorous form of Platonic rationalism. He was working on it, especially in his later years, but there is no sign that he ever got there.

In the immediate aftermath of his work on the incompleteness theorems came a number of naysayers and claim jumpers. The logician Ernst Zermelo is an example of the former type and the mathematician

Paul Finsler of the latter. Gödel must have found this extremely irritating. Indeed, his brother Rudolf stated that "shortly after the publication of his famous work," toward the end of 1931, Kurt had a severe psychological crisis and was thinking about suicide. Gödel's family was very worried about this, and Rudolf said the situation led to Kurt being committed against his will to a sanatorium in the Vienna suburb Purkersdorf bei Wien for a few weeks. John Dawson said, however, that this timeline of Gödel's activities casts some doubt on Rudolf's memory that Kurt stayed in a sanatorium at this point. Later stays at sanatoria, however, are documented.

6

Consequences of Incompleteness

There are some straightforward consequences of the incompleteness theorems for logic, mathematics, and computer science. There are also philosophical consequences and interpretations. The philosophical interpretations have ranged from the sublime to the ridiculous. Some of the worst are simply a function of being misinformed about what the theorems actually say. Another problem is that various positions Gödel never held or never would have held are sometimes attributed to him. I will, for the most part, discuss only Gödel's own philosophical interpretation of the incompleteness theorems. We now have a clearer understanding of how his views about the theorems matured over the years. This is due to the publication of his formerly unpublished writings and to items included in his literary estate. It will also be worthwhile to consider at least briefly some of the misinterpretations of his theorems.

Consequences for Logic, Mathematics, and Computer Science

The incompleteness theorems are limitative results concerning logic, mathematics, and theoretical computer science. They have a number of straightforward implications for these fields. As already mentioned, they spell the end of Hilbert's program in its original form. In particular, if F is finitist mathematics then there is no way to prove the consistency of F using F. One has to use more powerful mathematics. This means that one of the major schools in foundations of mathematics—Hilbertian formalism—was fatally flawed. If Hilbert's program had succeeded, then the landscape of logic and the foundations and philosophy of mathematics would be totally different today. The incompleteness theorems also meant that logicism in the style of Frege and Russell and Whitehead could not prevail. There could be no derivation of all mathematical truths from a universal set of axioms of "logic" as had been the logicists' goal. One could have consistency or completeness (or neither) but not both. In general, the theorems showed that there is a fundamental limitation on the power of axiomatic formal reasoning. The realm of mathematical truth cannot be regimented into systematic order, as originally intended, by setting out a single fixed set of axioms and rules of inference. We can formally deduce an endless number of truths from any given set of mathematical axioms and rules of inference that are independent of those axioms and rules if the system is consistent. Hence, the theorems come as a blow to anyone who thought the essence of mathematics was, in the end, axiomatic formal reasoning.

Since strict axiomatic formal systems can be understood as Turing machines, the incompleteness theorems also mean that there can be no computer—Turing machine—that could output all truths of mathematics if it is consistent. There are limitations on what can be done with algorithms. Leibniz's high hopes would have to be revised downward if, as is evidently the case, the *calculus ratiocinator* is to be understood in terms of an axiomatic formal system or Turing machine. Remarkably, Gödel had already said something very close to this to Carnap in 1929. There are also notes to this effect in his literary estate. For example, in one of these notes, Gödel says, "The universal characteristic claimed by Leibniz (1677) [if interpreted as a formal system] does not exist. Any systematic procedure for solving problems of all kinds would have to be nonmechanical."

Important consequences also relate set theory to arithmetic, as we will see in Chapter 8. When we add stronger and stronger axioms of infinity to set theory then, assuming their consistency, we can prove arithmetical theorems that could not be proved in the weaker systems. So these axioms have consequences for arithmetic. This is similar, up to a point, of adding Gödel sentences for systems to these systems, which allows us to prove more in the stronger system than we could prove in the weaker system.

In general, it would now be necessary to be aware of the difference between decidable and undecidable theories. One could set about investigating this in detail for many different kinds of formal theories. Moreover, in the modified forms of proof theory after Gödel, one could now investigate stronger and weaker systems of formal proof, along with the proof-theoretic strength of axiomatic formal systems required for consistency proofs for different kinds of systems. A lot of work has been done in this area. The theorems also raise questions about what can and cannot be done algorithmically, and they have thus played an important role in the theory of computability.

Gödel's Philosophical Interpretation of the Incompleteness Theorems

Gödel spent a lot of time thinking about his theorems' philosophical implications. In some of his writings, he contemplated the theorems against the much broader intellectual background that he was acquiring through his philosophical studies. We will see this, for example, in connection with his 1961 paper on Husserl, discussed in Chapter 11. Early on, he saw what the theorems pointed toward if one took Hilbert's philosophical distinctions seriously. Finitary mathematics F was supposed to be the domain of the concrete and what is immediately given in sensory intuition, which is "prior to all thought." Non-finitary reasoning in mathematics, Gödel said, was widely considered to be meaningful only insofar as it could be interpreted or justified in terms of finitary metamathematics. The "meaningful" part of mathematics was held to be the finitary part. In this view, mathematical symbols, which are meaningless in themselves, supposedly acquire a kind of substitute for meaning based on syntactical rules or conventions of use. Meaning is attributed solely to propositions that speak about concrete and finite objects, such as combinations of symbols. Transfinite mathematics itself was supposed to be meaningless.

By the second incompleteness theorem, if F is consistent, then the consistency of F cannot be proved using F but there can be consistency proofs for F. Such consistency proofs must involve infinitary notions that are now "abstract" or "ideal" instead of concrete. Now the objects involved could not be given immediately in sense perception. Also, they must embody some kind of meaning that cannot just be reduced to linguistic conventions about manipulating meaningless signs. Some kind of non-arbitrary, rational intuition of abstract, infinitary objects or structures must underwrite such proofs. This would have to be the source of evidence in mathematics. Purely formal proofs could not be the source of evidence unless the system in which they occur is consistent, but the evidence that any such formal system is consistent must come from outside the system by way of a stronger system. The same, in turn, is true of the new, stronger system. This suggests that, in the end, metamathematics must rest on something informal unless it terminates in a formalism that is not or cannot be discussed. It was part of Frege's logicism that we should eliminate appeals to intuition, but Gödel said that we would instead have to depend on and cultivate rational intuition.

For Gödel, all this points toward a Platonic rationalism involving informal rigor and to meaningful mathematics requiring intuition that goes beyond finitism. Gödel said:

> instead of clarifying the meanings of the non-finitary mathematical terms by explaining them in terms of syntactical rules, non-finitary terms are (used) in order to formulate the syntactical rules; and instead of justifying the mathematical axioms by reducing them to syntactical rules, these axioms (or at least some of them) are necessary in order to justify the syntactical rules (as consistent).

These words reflect Gödel's general picture of mathematics. What we are doing in mathematics is expressing abstract and non-finitary concepts in our definitions, axioms, and theorems. This is what underlies syntax in the first place. Later, Gödel contrasted the syntactical idea of meaning clarification in this passage with the idea of meaning clarification in Husserl's philosophy, and recommended that we go Husserl's way.

Gödel was aware that intuitionistic mathematics included more than finitist mathematics and yet was also distinct from Platonism. He went on to explore intuitionism and other forms of constructivism, but he also felt compelled to go beyond these. In set theory in particular (see Chapter 8), he argued that important metamathematical results require that we step beyond constructivism and embrace a platonic rationalism.

In the unpublished Gibbs lecture from 1951, later published in the *Collected Works*, and in various notes, Gödel also formulated the incompleteness theorems' implications as a disjunction:

> Either mathematics is incompleteable in this sense, that its evident axioms can never be comprised in a finite rule, that is to say, the human mind (even within the realm of pure mathematics) infinitely surpasses the powers of any finite machine, or else there exist absolutely unsolvable Diophantine problems . . .

By "Diophantine" he means, for our purposes, problems that are expressed in formulas of the type of the Gödel sentences. He allowed a simpler statement of this view to appear in the 1963 publication *Mathematics* in the *Life* magazine Science Library: "Either mathematics is too big for the human mind," he said, "or the human mind is more than a machine." Gödel cautiously formulated these as "either/or" sentences, but it is clear from other philosophical writings that he thought (1) the human mind *is* more than a (Turing) machine. It does not follow from the incompleteness theorems that minds are more than Turing machines, but Gödel said he hoped to prove rigorously that this was true. Later in his career, he said that he thought Husserl's phenomenology could help with this. Furthermore, he also came to believe that, if they are clearly stated, then (2) there are no *absolutely* unsolvable mathematical problems. Gödel linked both (1) and (2) to his Platonic rationalism.

The claim that there are no absolutely undecidable mathematical problems has been referred to as Gödel's "rationalistic optimism." If we do not identify the capacities of human reason with the capacities of computers (Turing machines), then we have no grounds to suppose they are subject to the same limitations. We do not know in advance what human reason is capable of, but we can circumscribe in advance the notion of Turing computability. Perhaps human reason can come to know more and more about the abstract, mind–independent world of mathematical objects and truths, whereas computers are not the kinds of things that can know about abstract objects and truths. Computers are just concrete syntax manipulators. This would have important implications for certain forms of artificial intelligence research. If humans can be conscious of abstract objects or meanings and computers in principle cannot, then we have located a fundamental difference between the two. We will see in Chapter 12 that in 1969 Gödel wrote a note on "Turing's philosophical error." That note argued that Turing was wrong to think mental procedures cannot carry further than mechanical procedures. In his famous paper "Computing Machinery and Intelligence," Turing had also argued that we would be able to build computers that would pass the "Turing test," originally called the "imitation game," for achieving human-level intelligence. Gödel, however, thought human "monads" could not be machines, but he does not claim that the incompleteness theorems prove this.

On the matter of absolute undecidability, it should be noted that Hilbert had also expressed an unbounded optimism about mathematical problem-solving. In 1900 and again in 1926 he wrote, "one of the things that attract us most when we apply ourselves to a mathematical problem is precisely that within us we always hear the call: here is the problem, search for the solution; you can find it by pure thought, for in mathematics there is no *ignorabimus*." He said, "The true reason why [no one] has succeeded in finding an unsolvable problem is, in my opinion, that there is *no* unsolvable problem. In contrast to the foolish *ignorabimus* our credo avers: We must know, We will know." These latter words, in German—*Wir müssen wissen, Wir werden wissen*—are in fact engraved on Hilbert's tombstone.

Gödel kept this optimism about mathematical problem-solving. Hilbert's mistake, he argued, was to construe this view about solvability in terms of computable (= mechanical) decidability in axiomatic formal systems, which is linked to the program of finitism. In a paper from the 1930s, Gödel said the incompleteness theorems could be interpreted as establishing that (1) certain problems are absolutely unsolvable or (2) that something was lost in the transition from understanding proof as something that provides evidence to understanding proof in the sense of pure formalism. Relying in part on the old distinction between form and content, he contrasts purely formal proofs with the contentual, abstract concept of proof as "that which provides evidence" and sides with (2). In this paper, he said we, therefore, cannot formalize mathematical evidence, even in the domain of number theory, but also said Hilbert's conviction that all mathematical problems are solvable remains untouched. It will not be possible to replace the human mathematician by a machine, even if we confine ourselves to number-theoretic problems.

In his 1961 manuscript on Husserl (see Chapter 11), Gödel said Hilbert's program was motivated by the one-sided empiricist or materialist *Zeitgeist* that has flourished since the Renaissance. The reason, he said, is that it depends strictly on finitary manipulation of concrete signs given to us in sensory experience. Thus, Gödel suggested that the incompleteness theorems disrupt the prevailing *Zeitgeist*. We can keep that optimism about mathematical problem solving if we do not analyze reason in terms of pure or blind calculation. In particular, Husserl's philosophy appears to allow for the possibility that we human "monads" can find non-arbitrary and finite but non-mechanical methods for deciding open mathematical problems. This would be based on clarifying the intuition of the abstract meanings of terms involved in the problems.

Although he does seem to have thought that the incompleteness theorems put an end to Leibniz's idea of the universal characteristic and *calculus ratiocinator*, if these are interpreted in terms of axiomatic formal systems—which is highly likely—Gödel may still have been influenced by Leibniz's rationalistic optimism. A cornerstone of Leibniz's philosophy is the "principle of sufficient reason," according to which there is a reason for the existence of everything. The universe is ordered, meaningful, and rational. For Leibniz, this is due to the nature of God.

Loss of Certainty and Mathematical Propositions 'True by Accident'?

Another issue often raised about the incompleteness theorems is whether they undermine the idea of the certainty or necessity of mathematical results. One could say the theorems show we cannot expect certainty or reliability *from purely formal proofs.* That is because one would need to know that the formal systems in which such proofs occur are consistent. That, in turn, would require insights that are independent of and more robust than what the systems contain. If we go to a stronger formal system, then knowledge of its consistency would require insights that are independent and even more robust. This process does not stop. We need to remind ourselves, however, that there was a long history of providing proofs in mathematics before strict formalism entered the scene. Relative to strict formalism, these proofs are informal or pre-formal and yet nonetheless rigorous. They manifest a kind of reasoning that is different from empirical investigation, but in the best cases do not seem to lack certainty or security. Surely a kind of informal rigor is involved in such proofs. Mathematics has been a subject which, for millennia, has had correct answers that you cannot really argue with if you know the definitions, prior theorems (if any), and so on. Mathematical problems had correct, univocal answers long before formalism appeared. Certainty or intrinsic necessity, one might say, is still an ideal in mathematics, even if we do not always have it at a given stage of research.

Of course, with strict formalism comes a sense in which we have great exactness and precision. One might try to argue that, for this reason, formalization and mechanization give us unparalleled clarity, and clarity should be required for certainty. The problem, as just mentioned, is that all this formal exactness does not always give us certainty. That is because we would need to know that the formal systems involved are consistent. For that, we must step outside the formal system in question. This means formal or computational exactness does not always yield certainty. To think otherwise is an illusion. The alleged clarity associated with formal systems is always clarity relative to some background against which the formal system is interpreted. It cannot be strict formalism—blind computation—all the way down. What could clarity amount to without meaning?

The incompleteness theorems certainly do not imply that axiomatic formalizations are worthless. They can help with precision, unification, clarity and other desiderata in mathematics. The point, rather, is that they just could not be the whole story about mathematics and logic. To some extent, it seems, a dialectical relationship can exist between formalization and rational intuition of abstract concepts. For example, when we formalize some concepts, then the formalization may suggest that further clarification is needed or it may suggest new concepts. This could lead to new or refined formalizations, and so on.

With some axiomatic formal systems such as ZF set theory, it is not known whether they are consistent or not. In fact, it would be extremely challenging to find consistency proofs for higher set theory. Gödel's response to this kind of situation was to point to the "empirical consistency" or "inductive consistency" of such systems. What this means is that they have existed for a number of years, have been developed in various ways and been scrutinized by researchers, have led to new results, and so on, without the appearance of any inconsistencies. Of course, this does not rule out the possibility that an inconsistency may be found in the future. Yet this inductive evidence presumably should not just count as nothing.

In a series of papers and books from the 1980s up to the first years of this century, the computer scientist Gregory Chaitin proved and reflected on a theorem in algorithmic information theory that, he has sometimes suggested, explains the incompleteness phenomenon. He has interpreted his theorem as showing that certain mathematical statements are "true for no reason," are "true by accident" or are "random." It is fairly easy to see what Gödel would think of this. Closer analysis of Chaitin's interpretation by Torkel Franzén and others shows that we are not entitled to say such things about mathematics. One way to see what Gödel's response would have been is to think about the two notions of proof that were distinguished a moment ago. On the "abstract" or "contentual" notion of proof, as distinct from the purely formal notion, the idea of "truth for no reason" makes no sense at all. Proofs in the contentual sense are all about human reason and evidence, but purely formal proofs are blind. Gödel would have us refrain from the assumption that (un)decidability by Turing machine = (un)decidability by human reason. He has at least some rudiments of an account of reason, whereas Chaitin does not address issues about the potential of human reason at all.

Logical Positivism, Carnap, and Wittgenstein

In the 1950s, Gödel applied his incompleteness theorems to the position that Carnap had developed in *The Logical Syntax of Language* (1934) and related works at that time, which Gödel summarized in the formulation "mathematics is syntax of language." Carnap's program, he said, aimed to establish three basic philosophical points: (1) That mathematical intuition, for all scientifically relevant purposes, can be replaced by conventions about the use of symbols. After 1959, Gödel would study Husserl's ideas on categorial intuition and intuition of essences in order to deepen his views on mathematical intuition. (2) Mathematics, unlike other sciences, does not describe any existing mathematical objects or facts. Rather, mathematical propositions, because they are nothing but consequences of conventions about the use of symbols and are therefore compatible with all possible experience, are void of content. (3) The conception of mathematics as a system of linguistic conventions makes the *a priori* validity of mathematics compatible with strict empiricism. It is allegedly possible to reconcile the *a priori* nature of mathematics and logic with empirical science by holding that the truths of mathematics and logic are based solely on linguistic (syntactical) conventions, while the truths of empirical science depend on verification in the world of sensory experience.

Gödel said his incompleteness theorems and some of his other mathematical results "tend to bring the falsehood of these assertions to light." Gödel's idea of applying his second incompleteness theorem to refute Carnap's view is clever: for the truths of mathematics to be based solely on linguistic (syntactical) conventions, the syntactical conventions must be consistent. If they are not consistent, then all statements will follow from them, including all empirical statements. A consistency proof will either be mathematical in nature or, stretching the term, empirical and inductive in nature. In either case, what is needed for the consistency proof undermines the logical positivists' conventionalism and nominalism. This kind of attempt by the logical positivists to transform philosophy into rigorous science thus fails. This does not imply, however, the failure of all possible attempts to develop philosophy as a rigorous, rational disciple. After 1958, Gödel was interested in the alternative that can be found in Husserl's work. Hao Wang told me that when he was meeting with Gödel, the two of them studied Husserl's essay "Philosophy as Rigorous Science" in order to explore this possibility.

A number of the logical positivists were influenced by Wittgenstein, and of course, Wittgenstein came to be very influential in philosophy in general. There was a period during which Wittgenstein was, in effect, something like a cult figure. Wang asked Gödel in 1972 about Wittgenstein's *Remarks on the Foundations of Mathematics* in which, among other things, Wittgenstein comments on the incompleteness theorems. In the answer, Wang reported, Gödel's habitual calmness was absent:

> Has Wittgenstein lost his mind? Does he mean it seriously? He intentionally utters trivially nonsensical statements. What he says about the set of all cardinal numbers reveals a perfectly naïve view. He has to take a position when he has no business to do so. For example, "you can't derive everything from a contradiction." . . . It's amazing that Turing could get anything out of discussions with somebody like Wittgenstein.
>
> He has given up the objective goal of making concepts and proofs precise. It is one thing to say that we can't make precise philosophical concepts . . . but to go further and say we can't even make mathematical concepts precise is much more . . . . To decline philosophy [in his later work] is an irrationalistic attitude. Then he declines all rationality—declining even science.

Wittgenstein's philosophical positions are not always easy to decipher, but it is clear that in his later work he was also an anti-Platonist. Could he be a rationalist, in the sense in which this has been discussed above? Here too the answer seems clear: no.

Abuses of the Incompleteness Theorems

The incompleteness theorems are rigorously proved *mathematical* theorems about the scope and limits of precisely defined axiomatic formal systems, or Turing machines, in which one can do some arithmetic. As mentioned above, Gödel made efforts to ensure they would be accepted by readers who subscribed to the different philosophical schools about the foundations of mathematics. One has to be much more careful about their alleged philosophical implications, and Gödel was cautious about how he formulated these. Some of the main problems in drawing philosophical consequences from the incompleteness theorems result from not knowing or understanding the point just mentioned, namely, that they apply to axiomatic formal systems or computers in which one can do arithmetic. Thus, they do not apply to many kinds of texts, such as religious texts—the Bible, Koran, Vedas, Buddhist sutras—and typically not even to theories in the natural sciences. The incompleteness theorems do not show that there are non-material souls, or that some kind of mystical intuition must replace cogent proof in mathematics. They do not provide grounds for despair or mystery-mongering. They do not show that the world in general, or the world of mathematics and logic in particular, is chaotic. They do not imply that truth is relative or accidental. They do not imply that there are only many different interpretations of things and no truth or objectivity. It is correct to say that formal proof is always relative to the axiomatic formal system in which it is defined but the incompleteness theorems drive a wedge between formal provability and mathematical truth. The theorems do not imply that there are absolutely unsolvable mathematical problems. Furthermore, Gödel pointed out that the original, contentual notion of proof is not the rigorously defined formal notion. Proofs in mathematics have been around for millennia, while strict formalism about proof has existed for only about a hundred years. The theorems do not imply any kind of anti-rationalism or irrationalism. Although they can be related in some ways to issues about free will versus determinism, they do not by themselves imply that free will exists.

Gödel would not have seen them as ushering in the "post-modern" age unless the post-modern age is supposed to be related to what computers or axiomatic formal systems provably cannot do. He did say, in effect, that he thought the theorems disrupt the empiricist or positivist *Zeitgeist*. To him, however, this was only fuel for adhering all the more resolutely to a kind of Platonic rationalism and objectivism. His Platonic rationalism was linked to his optimism about problem-solving. Philosophically, he was against naturalism, empiricism, conventionalism, nominalism and other "leftward" (see Chapter 11) views of mathematics and logic. He did speak of "intuition, " but this was *rational* intuition, which would involve systematic and finitary but non-algorithmic clarification of meanings. Intuition, on this view, is required for objectivity. We should expect open mathematical problems to be solvable in rigorous and non-arbitrary ways. Following Leibniz and Husserl, Gödel even hoped that philosophy would become a rigorous science of reason.

What often happens in dubious applications of the incompleteness theorems is that premises are missing that would be needed to derive the desired conclusions from the theorems themselves. Once one starts to fill these in, the problems arise. This happens even in the case of issues about minds and machines, where an extensive literature addresses how the theorems supposedly show outright that human minds are not computers. Gödel himself was cautious in his discussions of this, not drawing the kinds of conclusions about the mind found in the work of J.R. Lucas, Roger Penrose, and similar anti-mechanists. He did have his own anti-mechanist sentiments, but he did not claim to have mathematically closed off the possibility that minds are Turing machines, even if the theorems do close off the possibility of Turing machines for mathematics that are both consistent and complete.

7

Triumph, Travel and Tribulation

In 1932, Gödel submitted his famous incompleteness paper to the University of Vienna as his *Habilitationschrift*. Hahn wrote that it was

> a scientific achievement of the first rank . . . which will find its place in the history of mathematics . . . . The work submitted by Dr. Gödel surpasses by far the standard usually required for Habilitation. Today Dr. Gödel is already the principal authority in the field of symbolic logic and the foundations of mathematics.

Before the age of 25, Gödel had completed and published two very important papers. He also started to write some reviews. Menger said that, in the '30s, he was also studying philosophy, Leibniz in particular. Gödel's teachers and colleagues in Vienna helped in expeditiously disseminating his results. Word of his incompleteness paper was spreading, with acceptance and acclaim following soon after. Although Gödel was quickly becoming known for his work in Austria and abroad, his brother said that at home, among his family, he always went out of his way to "hide his light under a bushel."

Travel and Illness

The completion of the *Habilitationschrift* gave Gödel the right to teach as a *Privatdozent*. A *Privatdozent* is an unsalaried lecturer at a university who receives fees directly from the students who enroll in the lectures. In the summer semester of 1933, he first lectured on the foundations of arithmetic as a *Privatdozent* to about twenty students. Gödel went on to teach two more courses as a *Privatdozent* in 1935 and 1937, amidst the deteriorating situation in Vienna. Apart from two courses he later taught at Notre Dame University in the United States, this was the extent of Gödel's teaching experience. In 1939, while he was in the United States, the unpaid position of *Privatdozent* was abolished and replaced by a new paid position of *Dozent neuer Ordnung*. This change, with the position's name referring to the Nazis' "new order," was made once Nazi Germany annexed Austria. It required that he apply for the new position. Gödel did apply for this position, but it was approved only in 1940 after he had settled permanently in the United States. Applications for the position could be rejected on political or racial grounds. In Gödel's case, the delay in processing his application was evidently connected with questions about his associations with Jewish professors. His dissertation advisor, Hahn, was Jewish. A report on his application recognized that Gödel was apolitical but also noted that "to his discredit" he "always traveled in liberal-Jewish circles." The same report, however, suggested that he did not have many options given that "mathematics at that time [was] strongly Jewified." He had not displayed any support for the Nazis and this probably counted against him but, unlike his mother, he also was not known for making any statements against the Nazis. Marianne was opposed to the Nazis and was often incautious in her remarks about them.

Gödel's first visit to the United States took place during the 1933-34 academic year, when he was invited to the Institute for Advanced Study (IAS) in Princeton, N.J. The IAS came into being through the philanthropy of Louis Bamberger and his sister, Mrs. Felix Fuld, who had sold their department store business to the R.H. Macy company just before the stock market collapse that started the Great Depression. In consultation with the educational reformer Abraham Flexner, they set up the IAS, which began operations in 1933. During his first visit to the IAS in 1933-34, Gödel lectured on his incompleteness theorems. Stephen Kleene and J. Barkley Rosser, both later to become famous logicians, attended.

Gödel was lonely and depressed while in Princeton, and he was evidently not eating properly. He returned to Vienna in June of 1934. He had problems with his teeth during this period and said he felt wretched for a long time afterward. The trouble started with an inflammation of the jawbone due to a bad tooth. He blamed the problem on the dentist who had filled the tooth. He lost a lot of weight because of this, although digestive problems were probably partly to blame. Adding to the unpleasant situation at this time, Hans Hahn unexpectedly required urgent cancer surgery in June of 1934 and died at the age of 55.

In October, Gödel was admitted to a sanatorium near Vienna, Purkersdorf bei Wien. During this period the famous psychiatrist Julius Wagner-Jauregg was called in to consult on Gödel's case. He diagnosed a "nervous breakdown" due to overwork. The prognosis was that he should soon be able to recover.

Modern readers often wonder what, exactly, a sanatorium is. According to John Dawson, Gödel's leading biographer, "the Purkersdorf Sanatorium was an establishment for the well-to-do." It was "part spa and part rest home," and included "facilities for diet and rehabilitation therapy. It was not a mental institution in the modern sense but could provide a restful atmosphere and balanced regimen suited to recovery from physical and/or mental stress." Dawson said that, as such, it was an appropriate refuge for someone like Gödel who had an unstable temperament, was hypochondriacal, and could afford the treatment it offered. As a consequence of his treatment, Gödel had to postpone a return visit to Princeton until the autumn of 1935.

Karl Menger reported that Gödel was more withdrawn than before when he returned to Vienna from America. Once he started to participate in Menger's colloquium again, he was generous with advice and opinions on logical and mathematical questions. He perceived problematic points quickly and made replies with great precision, in a minimal number of words. In the process, he often opened up new perspectives for the inquirer. Menger said Gödel expressed all this as though it were completely a matter of course and often with a shyness whose charm awoke warm personal feelings in the listener.

The philosopher Edmund Husserl gave two lectures in Vienna in May 1935, but Gödel probably did not attend. He would begin to study Husserl's work in earnest only in 1959. In the summer of 1935, Gödel gave his second set of lectures at the University of Vienna.

Nine students enrolled in the course on selected topics in mathematical logic. In August 1935, he was in a sanatorium in the small Austrian town Breitenstein am Semmering. Dawson said this was more of an alpine health resort than a mental treatment facility. That fall, Gödel left Vienna for Princeton, but it was to be a short trip, the briefest of his three visits to the IAS. In November, he suddenly resigned from the IAS due to depression and overwork. He made his way to Paris and called his brother, hoping to be escorted back to Vienna. Rudolf evidently was unable to come to Paris on such short notice. Gödel stayed in Paris for three days and improved enough to take the train to Vienna by himself. It took a long time for him to recuperate. He was incapacitated until the spring of 1937. In 1936, he started again to spend periods in the Purkersdorf Sanatorium. For several months that year, he also stayed at a sanatorium for "nervous diseases" in Rekawinkel, like Breitenstein a small town in the province of Lower Austria. In June 1936, he stayed at some kind of institution in Golling bei Salzburg. He later wrote that 1936 was one of the three years when his health was exceptionally poor, the other years being 1961 and 1970. Yet he told Menger that he was working on his consistency proof for the generalized continuum hypothesis during 1936.

While on the way to his last lecture of the term at the University of Vienna on June 22, 1936, Moritz Schlick was assassinated. A mentally disturbed former student, a Dr. Hans Nelböck, shot him on the steps of a stairwell at the University. After this, the Vienna Circle's activities came to a halt. The Austrian Nazis tried to portray the crime as having been brought on by Schlick's "subversive" activities, but in fact, Nelböck acted out of his mental illness. This event must have had a terrible impact on Gödel.

By this time, Menger had decided to seek a position in America. The conditions in Vienna were becoming intolerable. In a letter, Menger said that he thought Austria's population probably contained no more than 45 percent Nazis but that the universities were 75 percent Nazi, and among the mathematicians with whom he interacted, it was not far from 100 percent.

In 1936, Gödel published a paper, "On the Length of Proofs." The paper showed that theorems with long proofs in a given system can be proved with much shorter proofs in a higher-level system. The logician George Boolos later gave an interesting example of this, in which a proof in first-order logic would require so many symbols that we would not be able to take it in, while it was relatively easy to follow the proof if it was presented in second-order logic. Gödel's result became a cornerstone in what was later known in computer science as complexity theory. It is also important as a fact about the human mind: there are cases where we would never see that a theorem is provable if we worked only in a weaker formal system but we can see it to be provable if we avail ourselves of a stronger system. It is revealed, in other words, that a sentence is provable but otherwise this fact would remain concealed. What the human mind can know is certainly not limited to what can be expressed only in lower-level systems, such as first-order logic. This is what a Platonic rationalist such as Gödel would expect.

In 1937, Gödel lectured for the last time at the University of Vienna, covering his own work on axiomatic set theory. His literary estate contains only one registration slip for this course, but some reports say five or six students attended the lectures. In December 1937, Gödel told Menger that he had proved the consistency of the generalized continuum hypothesis with the other axioms of set theory. He asked Menger not to divulge this to anyone, indicating that he had told only the Hungarian-born mathematician and physicist John von Neumann (1903-1957) about it. He also said he was trying to prove that the continuum hypothesis was independent of the other axioms, a task which he later abandoned in frustration.

Marriage and More Travel

Germany annexed Austria in March 1938. Gödel's circle of colleagues and friends in Vienna was changing significantly. By this time Hahn had died, Schlick had been assassinated, Menger had left to take a permanent position at Notre Dame University in the United States, Oskar Morgenstern and Abraham Wald had also departed to America, and Friedrich Waismann had gone to England.

In September 1938, Gödel and Adele were finally married after being together for more than ten years. The wedding was a private ceremony with only the families and a few other acquaintances as guests. Most of Gödel's friends and colleagues were unaware of his relationship with Adele, and it seems that some of them were taken aback by this development. Although some observers considered Kurt and Adele mismatched, it was also reported that the two were completely at ease with one another. Adele had no doubt already acquired experience with Kurt's mental and physical problems. She said later that before their marriage she had already been a taster for Kurt's food when he feared he might be poisoned. She acted as his protector when he thought noxious gasses were escaping from their refrigerator or when he displayed signs of depression or paranoia. Adele reportedly visited him during some of his stays in sanatoria.

Two weeks after their marriage, Gödel left for Princeton, where he lectured on his consistency proof for the axiom of choice and the generalized continuum hypothesis. In January 1939, he went to Notre Dame at Menger's invitation. There he lectured on his consistency results and also taught a course on elementary logic with Menger. The courses were offered as electives for graduate students only. Gödel's literary estate contains all these lectures, written in English. In letters to Menger in which he negotiated the visit to Notre Dame, Gödel expressed worries about the need to teach the introductory logic course. The text of these lectures on elementary logic is quite impressive. Imagine taking a course in elementary logic from the man who has been hailed as the greatest logician since Aristotle! At the time of this writing, these lectures still have not been published, but they deserve to be. The set theory course was a repeat of one he had just given at Princeton. His teaching responsibilities at Notre Dame were significantly greater than they had been in Vienna, and Menger had also set up a weekly symposium that both he and Gödel were to lead. Reports on Gödel's pedagogical style, which are few, suggest that he was not a wonderful teacher. His style was evidently to face the blackboard throughout his lectures. The introductory course at Notre Dame had about twenty students. Menger said Gödel seemed mostly healthy but not particularly happy during his stay at Notre Dame.

On this visit to America, Gödel met the logician Emil Post (1897-1954) at a 1938 conference in New York. Post described his meeting with Gödel as very emotional. Post had come close to obtaining the incompleteness theorems back in 1921, but this fact was recognized only much later when some of his work was published. After their meeting, Post wrote to Gödel that "perhaps the best I can say is that I would have *proved* Gödel's Theorem in 1921—had I been Gödel." In 1920, in his doctoral thesis, Post had proved the syntactic completeness of propositional logic, and later he went on to make other major contributions to logic and computability theory. On the basis of his work related to incompleteness, Post had reached the conclusion that "mathematical thinking is, and must be, essentially creative." The concept of "creative sets" in computability theory is due to Post. Post suffered from bipolar disorder, and in logic's wider circles, there was a considerable delay in acknowledging his work's novelty and significance.

When Gödel returned to Vienna in the summer of 1939, he was in for a shock. He was ordered to report for a physical examination for military service. World War II commenced on September 1, 1939, and the examination took place after this. To Gödel's surprise, he was found "fit for garrison duty." How could this be, with all of his health problems? Apparently, the responsible officials did not believe he had any heart problems from his childhood bout with rheumatic fever. John Dawson also noted that it is possible that the German authorities overlooked Gödel's episodes of mental instability, for if they had taken notice, Gödel might have met the fate the Nazis had in store for "mental defectives." In the same vein, Dawson pointed out, Gödel also felt the need to conceal his sanatorium visits from American immigration authorities.

During this period, Gödel's financial situation was deteriorating. He applied in November for a leave of absence to go to the United States on the grounds that he had no income. In a draft of a letter to the mathematician Oswald Veblen, who was at the IAS at this time, he asked for help to extract himself from his situation. The letter contains a crossed-out sentence about how he was beginning to look for a position in Vienna, perhaps in industry, since his savings would not sustain him for very long. He had no job because his *Dozent* application had not yet been approved. Meanwhile, he had been called up for military service. His situation in Vienna was looking dire. Even so, it is not clear that Gödel seriously expected to emigrate.

Although a lot of red tape was involved in getting German exit permits and U.S. visas, IAS Director Abraham Flexner and his successor Frank Aydelotte helped to expedite the whole process. The Gödels had their required papers and would depart for the United States in 1940. After moving to Princeton, Gödel would never again return to Europe. In fact, he did not travel much at all. Adele, however, returned to Europe on numerous occasions. She probably had a very lonely life in Princeton, and it seems she had few friends there.

We know that Gödel was studying Leibniz in 1938 and 1939. In 1939, he told Menger that he believed some of the Leibniz's important writings not only had not been published but had been destroyed in manuscript. He developed the view that there was some kind of conspiracy against Leibniz. When Menger asked him in 1939 who would have an interest in destroying Leibniz's writings, Gödel replied, "Naturally those people who do not want men to become more intelligent." When Menger suggested that Voltaire would be a more likely target, Gödel responded by asking, "Who would ever become more intelligent by reading Voltaire's writings"! In the 1950s or later, in a conversation with Oskar Morgenstern, Menger discussed Gödel's ideas about the destruction of Leibniz's writings. Morgenstern related an interesting story. He said that one day Gödel took him to the Princeton University Library and "gathered together an abundance of really astonishing material." This material consisted, on the one hand, of books and articles with references to Leibniz's writings and, on the other, the series or collections those works referred to. The cited writings, however, were all missing in one strange manner or another. Even Morgenstern said this material was "highly astonishing."

The situation in Vienna was only worsening with political and economic upheavals, persecutions, and various Nazi activities. In November 1939, while walking near the University, Gödel was attacked by a group of young Nazis. They knocked off his glasses, but Adele helped to drive them off with blows from her umbrella. It seems he was either mistaken for a Jew, or he was thought to be someone who fraternized with Jews, or he was attacked because he was an intellectual. He was not injured but the incident, in spite of his otherworldliness, must have made an impression on him.

Meanwhile, Gödel had been making progress with some very challenging problems in set theory.

8

Now, Set Theory

ödel had already started to think about the continuum problem
in set theory in 1930, and this persisted through the late 30s and
beyond. It was in the middle and late 30s that he proved the consistency
of the axiom of choice and the continuum hypothesis with the other
axioms of Zermelo-Fraenkel set theory. His incompleteness theorems
already constituted a profound contribution to mathematical logic and
would have established him as one of the greatest logicians of all time.
Now, with the continuum problem, he turned to an unsolved problem
in the deep subject of set theory. We will have a brief look at this
fascinating area of mathematics. To understand Gödel's technical
achievement here and his developing philosophy of set theory, we need
a little more background. There are different set theories, but Gödel
worked with the standard axiomatic formal system, ZF, that derives
from Georg Cantor's work. ZF is central to the foundations of
mathematics. Later on, he also worked with what is called von
Neumann–Bernays–Gödel set theory.

Cantorian Set Theory

The continuum problem has its origins in the work of the great
mathematician Georg Cantor. Cantor created modern set theory, with
its rigorous mathematical treatment of infinity. This work completely
revolutionized thinking about the infinite, so much so that he met with
some virulent opposition. This no doubt affected his delicate mental
health. Cantor was to spend significant amounts of time in "nerve
clinics." Some mathematicians at the time, however, including very
famous figures such as Hilbert, embraced and promoted Cantorian
set theory. We saw earlier how Hilbert remarked that no one shall

drive us from "Cantor's paradise." Hilbert thought the continuum problem was so important that he placed it first on his famous list of open mathematical problems at the Second International Congress of Mathematicians in Paris in 1900. With our entry into Cantor's paradise, we will start to see all sorts of important differences between the finite and the infinite. The finite has always seemed more tangible to us, something we can readily understand. This fact was at the source of much of the original opposition to Cantor's work, but we shall soon be exploring some of the terrain of the infinite.

Problems about continuity are very old in mathematics and philosophy. If we think of a line geometrically, it appears to be a continuous entity. Consider how you would actually draw a line. It is not chopped up into discrete bits, but we construct it in a flow, continuously. In set theory, the continuum problem can be stated in some different ways that are equivalent to one another in extension. (Extensionality, as Zermelo defined it, is discussed below.) One simple way of putting it is to ask how many points there are on a straight line in Euclidean space. Here the idea is to think of points on the line as real numbers. There are no "gaps" between the real numbers as there are between the discrete natural numbers. The continuum problem can be stated precisely in the context of Cantorian set theory, as we will see momentarily.

Cantor was not working in axiomatic set theory. Set theory was first axiomatized by Ernst Zermelo, then in improved formulations by Abraham Fraenkel and others. Zermelo's axiomatization antedated the delineation of first-order logic, but he set it up to avoid paradoxes. He replaced the axiom that led to the paradoxes, usually called the naïve comprehension axiom, with what he called the "axiom of separation." This did not allow sets to be independently defined, as in Frege's Basic Law V, but only to be separated as subsets from sets already given. In this case, one could exclude contradictory notions such as the set of all sets, the set of all ordinal numbers, and Russell's set of all non-self-membered sets. Although the standard paradoxes are blocked by this move, it is not known whether ZF is consistent. What we can do is to appeal to the "empirical" or "inductive" consistency of ZF, as this was described in Chapter 6.

Cantorian set theory starts with some deceptively simple characterizations of what sets are supposed to be. One of these characterizations is that a *set* is any collection into a whole *M* of definite and separate objects *m* of our intuition or thought. The upper-case *M* denotes the object—the set—that is obtained from objects denoted by the lower-case letter *m*. Another characterization is that a set is any Multiplicity that can be thought of or collected into a One. These characterizations use the term *"any"* multiplicity or collection, and it is this "any" that leads into the rarefied heights of set theory. In particular, it includes both finite and different kinds of infinite multiplicities. Mathematics, of course, is full of references to infinity. There are, for example, infinitely many natural numbers, infinitely many rational numbers, infinitely many real numbers, and so on. So these simple characterizations of the concept of set are very general, and subsequent work has shown how much hidden meaning they in fact possess. It is safe to say that we still do not have anything like a full clarification of the meaning of these characterizations, although there is plenty to get us started.

First, if we have some objects a, b, c, d, for example, then we collect these into a set by simply placing brackets around the objects, $\{a,b,c,d\}$, which are now regarded as members or elements of the set. We can then name the set, for example, $B = \{a,b,c,d\}$. To say that a, for instance, is an *element* (*member*) of B we write a $\in$ B. Once we have sets such as B we can define lots of properties and relations of sets. One important relation is the subset relation. A set A is a *subset* of a set B in the following case: if an object is in A then it is in B. Thus, $\{a,b\}$ is a subset of $\{a,b,c,d\}$, and so is $\{b\}$. On this definition, $\{a,b,c,d\}$ is also a subset of $\{a,b,c,d\}$. Sets are *identical*, $=$, when they have the same members, irrespective of order. When Zermelo later axiomatized set theory, this notion of identity was set forth as an axiom called the *axiom of extensionality*. We can also define proper subsets. A set A is a *proper subset* of a set B when it is a subset of B but $A \neq B$. So $\{a,b,c,d\}$ is of course not a proper subset of $\{a,b,c,d\}$, but, for example, $\{c,d\}$ is.

With another simple notion, we can already get some significant traction in set theory. This is the notion of a *1-to-1 correlation* of members of sets. The members of the set $\{a,b,c\}$, for example, can be put into 1-to-1 correlation with the set $\{1,2,3\}$, but cannot be put into 1-to-1 correlation with the set $\{1,2\}$. Notice in particular that no finite set can be put into 1-to-1 correlation with a proper subset of itself. This can be taken as a defining characteristic of finite sets. The mathematician Richard Dedekind (1831-1916) just turned this around to give us the first definition of infinite sets: A set is *infinite* only in the case that it can be put into 1-to-1 correlation with a proper subset of itself. This may seem strange at first, but it is part of what is involved in getting our heads around the infinite. For example, all the even natural numbers form an infinite set $\{0,2,4,6, . . 2n, . . .\}$, all of the natural numbers $\{0,1,2,3, . . n, . . .\}$ form an infinite set, the even numbers are clearly a proper subset of all the natural numbers, and yet it is easy to establish a 1-to-1 correlation between these sets. We can give a simple formula that establishes the correlation. Just pair each n in the set of natural numbers with $2n$ in the set of even natural numbers.

Cantor proved a fundamental theorem that really launches the enterprise of higher set theory. We know there are infinitely many natural numbers, and also that there are infinitely many real numbers. Sets are the *same size* or have the *same cardinality* only if their members can be put into 1-to-1 correlation. We will use the symbol "$\approx$" as in $A \approx B$, to say that A and B are the same size. The term "cardinality" here just refers to the idea of cardinal numbers, that is, answers to the question "How many?" Cantor asked whether the set of natural numbers is the same size as the set of real numbers. Recall that numbers such as 3/4, 1/3, π, and so on are real numbers, but they are not natural numbers. It might seem as though there should be more real numbers than natural numbers, but many people balk at this because if it is true, then there are at least two sizes of infinity. In fact, that is just what Cantor proves in an elegant and relatively simple argument using a technique called "diagonalization." So there are at least two sizes of infinity. This leads to an important distinction: some infinities are *denumerable* and some are *non-denumerable*. Denumerable infinities are those that can be put into 1-to-1 correspondence with the set of natural numbers, whereas non-denumerable infinities cannot. Non-denumerable infinities have more members than denumerable infinities. The set of real numbers is a non-denumerable infinity.

Cantor then proved another theorem that is even more mind-blowing, and this theorem figures essentially into Gödel's work on the continuum problem. We need the definition of a "power set" to grasp this theorem. The *power set* P(A) of a set A is the set of all subsets of A. Among the sets of set theory it is typical to include the *empty set*, which we can designate with the symbol φ (or { }). We think of this as the set that has no members. The empty set is regarded as a subset of every set. Now we can give examples of power sets. For example, if A = {1,2} then we first form all of the subsets of A and then collect them together into a set. The subsets are φ, {1}, {2}, {1,2}, and collecting these into a whole we have the set P(A) = { φ, {1}, {2}, {1,2}}. Note that A has two members but P(A) has four members. Looking at the finite case, the name "power set" derives from the fact that if a set has n members, then its power set will always have $2n$ members. Will this transfer to infinite sets? Yes.

To see this, we should first look at what is called Cantor's Theorem. Cantor proved that for any set A, the power set of A is always larger than A. It always has more members. Thus, consider the set of natural numbers N. It is an infinite set. By Cantor's Theorem, the set P(N) exists and it is larger than N. We can iterate the power set operation over and over. Since P(N) is a set, P(P(N)) exists by Cantor's Theorem. Since P(P(N)) exists, so does P(P(P(N))). Where does this end? It doesn't end. There are infinitely many sizes of infinity! So here we have a sequence of infinite sets that we obtain with the power set operation.

Cantor uses the term "transfinite" for sets and numbers that go beyond finite sets and numbers. The natural numbers 0, 1, 2, 3, 4 . . . are finite cardinal numbers. When Cantor first developed set theory, he put forth some generating principles to show how we can obtain, he hoped, all and only the transfinite numbers. He started with transfinite ordinal numbers. In the case of ordinals, the ordering of the members matters. Number terms are used as ordinals when we refer explicitly to the ordering of objects, as when we say there is a first, second, third, and so on, instead of simply saying there is one, or two or three. Cantor then defined the transfinite cardinals in a uniform way on the basis of the ordinals. He named the first transfinite cardinal number $\aleph_0$. ($\aleph$ pronounced "aleph," is the first letter of the Hebrew alphabet.) It is the number of the set of natural numbers $\{0, 1, 2, 3, 4 \ldots\}$, irrespective of their order. (Actually, of any set $\approx$ to the set of natural numbers). So it is larger than any natural number but is the first number to come after all of the natural numbers. The next transfinite number after that is $\aleph_1$, then $\aleph_2$, $\aleph_3$, and so on indefinitely. Each one is supposed to be the next greatest after the number it follows. Cantor wanted to establish that every transfinite cardinal number was a member of the system of alephs $\aleph_0, \aleph_1, \aleph_2, \aleph_3, \aleph_4, \ldots$, and that there were none outside of this ordering. The transfinite cardinals, he thought, should have the same ordering principle as the real numbers. That is, for any two of them x and y, we should have either $x = y$ or $x < y$ or $y < x$. This is related to the *well-ordering principle* that says every set can be well-ordered.

The Continuum Problem

It was known in Cantor's time that the set of all real numbers was the same size as the set of all subsets of the natural numbers; in other words, the same as the power set of the set of natural numbers. The cardinal number of the real line, that is, of the continuum, is often denoted as C. It is fairly easy to show that $C = 2^{\aleph_0}$. But which $\aleph$ is $2^{\aleph_0}$?

We have two different sequences of transfinite objects, the power set sequence on the one hand and the aleph sequence $\aleph_0, \aleph_1, \aleph_2, \aleph_3, \aleph_4, \ldots$, on the other. We use different operations and concepts to arrive at these. It is natural to ask how these sequences are related to one another. There is no guarantee that every cardinality in the power set sequence will have a representative among the transfinite number classes $\aleph_1, \aleph_2, \aleph_3, \aleph_4 \ldots$ Cantor needed to prove the well-ordering principle for his aleph sequence. This, in turn, is required if there is to be any hope of making progress on the continuum problem.

If we consider the finite case, it is easy to see that there are cardinal numbers between 21 and 22, 22 and 23, and so on. The finite cardinal numbers are $0, 1, 2, 3, 4, \ldots$. But what happens in the transfinite case? We can finally state the continuum problem in the language of set theory. We know that $C = 2^{\aleph_0}$. Now which of the alephs $\aleph_1, \aleph_2, \aleph_3,$ $\aleph_4, \ldots$ is $2^{\aleph_0}$? Which transfinite cardinal is the size of the continuum? How many points, in terms of the transfinite numbers, are there on the line? Cantor conjectured that $2^{\aleph_0} = \aleph_1$. So this is Cantor's *continuum hypothesis*, CH, but try as he might he could not prove it. We know that the cardinality of $C = 2^{\aleph_0}$, and so could not be $\aleph_0$, but is there another aleph that lies between $\aleph_0$ and C? The answer to this question would have significant consequences for mathematics, which is why Hilbert placed it on his list of the most important open problems in mathematics. Some mathematicians thought there were other alephs between $\aleph_0$ and C, and some still do. The problem is still unsolved and, as we will see, there is a lot of controversy and uncertainty about it. Gödel weighed in on this and, as one might expect, his views were again shaped by some deep philosophical thinking. The CH was quickly generalized, as is common in mathematics: the *generalized continuum hypothesis* is the statement that $2^{\aleph_\alpha} = \aleph_{\alpha + 1}$.

Cantor struggled with the CH for a number of years. He initially believed that $2^{\aleph_0} = \aleph_1$ but he could not prove it. Later, he changed his mind. He thought he had various proofs but then realized they were worthless. At one point he was convinced that C was greater than any of the alephs, in other words, that there were infinitely many alephs between $\aleph_0$ and C! Cantor kept changing his mind about the CH. He suffered his first serious nervous breakdown in the midst of his efforts. What Cantor did not know was that in the framework of set theory existing at the time, it was impossible to solve the continuum problem, unless he had been able to conjure up some entirely new principle that no one has yet found. Cantor had not axiomatized his set theory, but others in his wake had. We now know, thanks to the work of Gödel and Paul Cohen (1934–2007), that the CH cannot be decided on the basis of set theory's existing principles. Neither CH nor its negation can be proved. It is a statement that is independent of the existing axioms. Some entirely new axiom or axioms will be needed. Gödel made a number of interesting suggestions about this.

Gödel's Relative Consistency Theorem

The key axiom in Gödel's consistency theorem is the *axiom of choice* *(AC)*. AC is not included as an axiom of ZF itself. Instead, we can just write ZFC when we want to include it.

Axiom of Choice: If A is a set, all of whose elements are non-empty sets, no two of which have any elements in common, then there exists a set C that has one element in common with each element of A.

The axiom of choice has been controversial ever since Zermelo first formulated it. The reason has to do with the shift from the finite to the infinite. The axiom says that there exists a choice set C that contains one element from each member of a given set A of non-empty disjoint sets but it gives no indication of how the selection is to be made. It seems that in principle we could make a finite number of choices, but no one can actually make an infinite number of choices. With the AC there is no way to prescribe how to make the infinitely many choices. This is an objection that stems from constructivist worries. Proofs, for example, need to be finite in some sense. We use a finite number of steps to obtain a theorem from some axioms, but how could I complete a proof if I have to use an infinite sequence of choices to obtain a choice set at a step in a proof?

Zermelo defended the AC by pointing out that it had already been used implicitly by mathematicians. A host of important and interesting results, in fact, depended on it. It was also Zermelo who succeeded in proving the well-ordering theorem. It was in connection with reflection on this proof that he first formulated the AC. As it turned out, the well-ordering principle was shown to be (extensionally) equivalent to the AC. In fact, there are now many known equivalents to the AC. With the proof of the well-ordering theorem, one can finally confer sense or meaning on the CH that makes it look precise enough to constitute a genuine open problem in mathematics. That is because now it should be possible to place $2^{\aleph_0}$ among the *ordered alephs*. So in Gödel's proof of the consistency of the AC and the CH with the other axioms of set theory, the combination of AC and CH is not accidental. There is a direct rational connection. The AC is needed in order to constitute non-arbitrarily the meaning of the CH as a problem in the first place.

Gödel gave a philosophical defense of the AC to accompany his remarkable technical result. His *philosophical* response was to invoke his Platonic rationalism. That is, in the first place we should not think of the "choice set" as constituted by our infinitely many choices. We do not, as it were, constitute it successively through time but, rather, its elements exist simultaneously, i.e., atemporally or omnitemporally. According to this philosophy, we view all the axioms of set theory, including AC, as making meaningful assertions about what exists, mind-independently and atemporally. That is how the meaning of the axioms is constituted in classical set theory. The choice set exists independently of our constructions or our finite abilities. It already exists as a completed object. The claim is that there are abstract, actual complete infinite totalities that exist independently of human minds. In the Platonist view, we discover such objects. We do not invent them. For Gödel, we discover facts about the set-theoretic universe through structured, non-arbitrary rational intuition, not through some haphazard or "mystical" insight. Seeing that the meaning of CH depends on AC is an example of rational intuition. Especially in his later writings, Gödel said we need to clarify further the meaning of set theory's concepts. This is one of the places in his later thinking where he looks to the philosopher Husserl for help in formulating a defensible platonic rationalism. The worry about proofs being finite would be addressed by holding as follows. In proofs, in a pre-formal or non-formalistic sense, we do not appeal to meaningless finite sequences of signs but rather to the *meanings* of the sign configurations. These meanings will be expressed in a finite number of concrete symbols, but that is not all there is to proof in the contentual sense. A proof is associated with a network of abstract concepts. This is what Gödel in some writings referred to as the "abstract" concept of proof, the concept of proof as "that which provides evidence."

It is Gödel's own technical result on the consistency of the AC with the other axioms of ZF set theory that really helps us to have more confidence in the AC. So again we see that Gödel had both philosophical and technical reasons for retaining the AC.

Gödel's striking theorem, the result of intense effort on his part, can be stated simply:

Theorem: ZF + AC + CH is consistent.

In fact, he proved this theorem for the GCH. This is the *technical* reason for not discarding the AC. If the axioms of ZF are consistent then adding AC and GCH to them will not lead to any contradictions. This offers some measure of assurance about the axiom that we would not have had otherwise, and it is an important response to the critics of the AC. It also shows that we cannot disprove the GCH.

It is worthwhile to consider Gödel's comments about how he finally got this proof. It was his Platonic heuristic at work again. He had read Hilbert's alleged solution to the continuum problem around 1930. This was in fact not a solution at all, but it got Gödel started on the problem. He experimented with building up enough ordinals on constructive grounds in order to devise a model of set theory in which AC and CH would also be true. In so doing he was probing how far he could get without using Platonist assumptions. Finally, he realized that he could get the model he wanted if he supposed that *all the classical ordinals* were given. Philosophically, however, this involves a shift from a constructivist approach to a Platonic rationalism. Now he gets his result, but it requires a particular philosophical view about what exists in set theory that cannot be obtained from constructivism. He does not use what is typically regarded as the full universe of set theory that is based on the so-called "iterative" conception of sets. Instead of this full "cumulative hierarchy" he uses a thinner, reduced version that is more tractable and for which there is arguably better evidence. This yields what is usually referred to as an "inner model" of set theory. Some features of this inner model, however, still transcend standard constructive limitations. In later writings, Gödel was always committed to the full universe of the "maximal" iterative conception of set.

In a number of cases, Gödel wants to start his research with a constructive approach. For example, can we give a constructive but non-finitist consistency proof for arithmetic? The answer is "yes." Now in set theory, can we get enough ordinals constructively to show that AC and CH are consistent with the axioms of ZF? One could try, but it does not work. Then he takes all the classical ordinals as given and is able to get his result. The lesson, according to Gödel, is that if we take all the classical ordinals as given, as a Platonist would, then we are able to be directed toward and to see rationally and non-arbitrarily (that is, intuit) something we would otherwise not have been able to intuit. A metamathematical result is revealed that otherwise would have remained concealed.

CH is Independent of the ZF Axioms

Gödel's theorem on AC and CH does not show that we can prove CH, but now we at least know it is consistent with the other axioms. Gödel thought AC and CH were probably independent of ZF and he worked for a number of years trying to prove this. It was the mathematician Paul Cohen, however, who succeeded in 1963. Cohen showed that the negation of AC and the negation of CH are also consistent with the axioms of ZF. Thus, we cannot prove CH, but we also cannot prove ¬ CH on the basis of the existing axioms. Gödel showed that whether CH is true or not, it is at least not disprovable from the accepted axioms of set theory if these axioms are consistent. Cohen showed that even if true, this is not provable either.

Gödel said that Cohen's results did not cause him to retract any of the ideas he had expressed in his famous paper, "What is Cantor's Continuum Hypothesis?" He continued to suspect that the CH would turn out to be false and that new axioms would be discovered from which it could be disproved. He did not give up hope for a solution to the continuum problem.

After Cohen, however, the question of the cardinality of C became more puzzling than ever. What could C be? It could be $\aleph_2$, or $\aleph_3$, or $\aleph_{101}$, or just about as big as we like! The matter was left wide open, although work since the time of Gödel and Cohen has continued and has led to further results. Cohen also came to doubt the truth of the CH. The Gödel and Cohen results together show that we have not fully clarified the concept of set in the simple "definitions" given above.

Many results in mathematics and logic do not demand fundamental thinking about what they mean for the field or about how mathematicians should proceed in their wake. The independence results, however, have had just this effect. They are results that show us we are at the edge of research in a deep and difficult field. They demand new and creative thinking about this field of mathematics. Somehow, we will have to imagine new possibilities from which we might filter out necessities. Gödel said the situation with CH would require a deeper analysis of meaning than mathematicians are used to giving. This, I think, creates a whole new sociology of the problem. It might make it harder to obtain funding to work on the problem, and younger mathematicians who need to publish results to obtain jobs and tenure are probably less likely to tackle it. It will require uncommon skills.

Gödel was a rationalistic optimist about solving the continuum problem. In his 1964 paper on the continuum hypothesis, he said,

> For someone who considers mathematical objects to exist independently of our constructions and of our having an intuition of them individually, and who requires only that the general mathematical concepts must be sufficiently clear for us to be able to recognize their soundness and the truth of the axioms there is, I believe, a satisfactory foundation of Cantor's set theory in its whole original extent and meaning.

And,

> The set-theoretical concepts and theorems describe some well-determined reality, in which Cantor's conjecture must be either true or false. Hence, its undecidability from the axioms being assumed today can only mean that these axioms do not contain a complete description of that reality.

Gödel's idea for finding new axioms in set theory was to suggest that we add large cardinal axioms to the existing axioms of ZFC, although he also said other types of axioms might be possible. Large cardinal axioms are just strong axioms of infinity. The iterative concept of set permits unlimited extensions. This makes axioms of infinity look attractive because they can be introduced without arbitrariness.

Gödel argued that other grounds would also support certain axioms over others. This would depend on what he called extrinsic evidence or on what Wang called "pragmatic success." Gödel distinguished intrinsic evidence from extrinsic evidence. The former kind of evidence is associated with "analyticity." It is supposed to depend only on *meaning* and not on the way the world is. With intrinsic evidence, we are unfolding the meaning of concepts, and for Gödel, this was a matter of rational intuition. This need not always yield an immediate and self-evident truth. One might have to handle the concepts for a while before they become a self-evident truth. With extrinsic evidence, however, the idea is to accept an axiom or axioms by "inductively studying [their] success." "Success" means something like explanatory power or predictive success. Hence, we appeal to their mathematical consequences. For example, we might find a proof that contracts many proofs into one, or statements provable by cumbersome means might have proofs that are simpler and easier to understand. But he goes further:

> A much higher degree of verification than that, however, is conceivable. There might exist axioms so abundant in their verifiable consequences, shedding so much light upon a whole field, and yielding such powerful methods for solving problems . . . that no matter whether they are intrinsically necessary, they would have to be accepted at least in the same sense as any well-established physical theory.

Now it would not be intrinsic meaning alone but extrinsic evidence that would suggest axioms.

Gödel noted how large cardinal axioms, on the assumption of their consistency, yield new arithmetic theorems. This is again related to what the incompleteness theorems tell us, up to a point. When we add stronger and stronger axioms of infinity to set theory, then we can prove arithmetical theorems that could not be proved in the weaker systems. So the axioms have consequences for arithmetic. Gödel said the consequences of large cardinal axioms for arithmetic or for finite mathematics could be so abundant and enlightening that we might consider accepting them even though they are not evident as assertions about the existence of infinite sets. The evidence for the axioms, in this case, would not be intrinsic, or at least not exclusively so.

These comments of Gödel's, however, have generated a lot of discussion. Are we supposed to regard *extrinsic* evidence as sufficient for solving open *mathematical* problems such as CH? If so, there would be huge implications for mathematics, because standard solutions to purely mathematical problems have never been regarded as inductive or merely pragmatic. It is not clear what Gödel really had in mind in this last comment. How does it gibe with his position on intrinsic necessity, meaning clarification and rational intuition? What is the relationship between intrinsic necessity and extrinsic evidence supposed to be? One suggestion, put forward by Wang, is that extrinsic support is only supposed to give provisional evidence that could be used to reach intrinsic necessity.

Many researchers have followed up on Gödel's suggestion that we look to large cardinal axioms. Many results have been obtained from this, but it appears that the large cardinal program is not going to help settle the CH. Subsequent work by the French mathematician Paul Levy and the American set-theory specialist Robert Solovay and others basically shows that CH is independent of ZFC + "any large cardinal axioms."

Like Cantor, Gödel came to think that the CH was false, but he changed his mind about it several times. It is curious that while wrestling with the continuum hypothesis both Cantor and Gödel experienced serious mental health problems. Was this just a coincidence or did it have something to do with working on a very hard problem that would not yield? There is a Buddhist idea that if we think we *must* do something *and* we are unable to do it, then this will result in *Dukkha* (usually translated as "suffering"). I think it is safe to say that Gödel found work on the problem to be exhausting, and as time went on, extremely frustrating.

Later in life, as we will see, Gödel prepared some additional work on the continuum problem but, uncharacteristically, it contained serious errors, and he withdrew it. Gödel said he was taking various medicines at the time that clouded his mind.

9

Moving to America

At the beginning of 1940, Kurt and Adele left Vienna for America. They traveled east and boarded the trans–Siberian railway, which took them all the way across Russia. From there they went to Yokohama and then embarked on a ship to San Francisco. An Atlantic crossing at this time would either not have been possible at all or would have been too dangerous. After arriving in San Francisco in early March, they continued by train to Princeton. Years later, Adele recalled their trip out of Europe and through Russia as very stressful. She said they frequently traveled at night and were constantly worried about being stopped and turned back.

Arrival in Princeton

There were to be significant changes in Gödel's life and work with his arrival in Princeton. The period leading up to his move to Princeton must have been exasperating and quite exhausting. Now the tumult of Vienna would be left behind, as would the frequent travel. Gödel had lived in Europe for 34 years and would have another 38 in America. He had lived in Vienna, in particular, from age 18 until 34. He would henceforth travel very little, never return to Europe, and experience no further great changes in the external conditions of his life. The Vienna period had been very fruitful. His major results in logic and foundations of mathematics were produced there. The work on set theory had somehow been completed during his travels to the United States and bouts of poor health. Gödel did not publish as much after he moved to the IAS even though he had no teaching duties and, during his early years there, no administrative chores. His papers and lectures were mostly written in response to invitations.

Although Gödel had always read philosophy, this began to play a more central role in his life after 1940, especially around 1943. He started to develop a rather grand vision of what metaphysics should look like, but there are only hints of what it would consist of. In later years, he told Hao Wang it would be a monadology in the style of Leibniz but developed using the transcendental eidetic method of Husserl. Husserl himself had begun to speak of monads in his phenomenology around 1910. For Leibniz, what is real are monads, and monads are simple, active non-material entities that have memory, perceptions, and appetites. Some monads also have "apperception" or reason. Human beings are monads of this latter type. Leibniz said monads are governed by laws of final causes, in which essential reference is made to goals, and they are not governed by laws of efficient causes. Teleological explanation, which is explanation that makes reference to goals or purposes, is officially supposed to be avoided in modern science. Modern science is to appeal, where possible, only to efficient causes. Husserl also wrote about how we humans, as transcendental egos, are monads. On the basis of Husserl's methodology, however, it is not clear that we could have evidence for monads as non-material entities, even though Husserl did argue against scientific reductionism about human beings.

Among Gödel's first acquaintances in Princeton was Oskar Morgenstern. In addition to other work, Morgenstern was known for the influential book that he wrote with von Neumann, *Theory of Games and Economic Behavior*. Morgenstern had emigrated to America from Vienna in 1938 and had taken a position at Princeton University. Albert Einstein became a very good friend of Gödel; after Einstein died, Morgenstern became especially close to Gödel. Some of the first impressions that Morgenstern recorded concerned his puzzlement at how Kurt had come to be married to Adele. He thought it would be difficult for Adele to be accepted in Princeton society, and said it was almost impossible to speak to Gödel when Adele was present. He described Adele as "a Viennese washerwoman type: garrulous, uncultured, [and] strong-willed." He conceded, however, that Gödel seemed to be in better spirits when in Adele's company than at other times. He conjectured that she "had probably saved his life" and, in any case, that Gödel was "a bit crazy." Morgenstern did not mention that Adele had a sharp and rather wicked sense of humor. She could be quite funny and perceptive, albeit usually with a caustic bite.

Morgenstern was also surprised to learn of Kurt's interest in ghosts. Gödel had apparently already developed an interest in parapsychological phenomena when he was a university student, but then so had some of the Vienna Circle's members, including Carnap and Hahn. It has been said that Gödel believed in the possibility of telepathy. The logician Georg Kreisel has written that Gödel was also interested in demonology and angelology.

Gödel was initially an "ordinary member" of the IAS from 1940 to 1946, on annual appointments. He became a permanent member in 1946 and a professor in 1953. Many commentators on Gödel's career have wondered why it took so long for him to be made a permanent member and, especially, a professor. He was one of the stars at the IAS, Einstein's best friend after 1942, and yet he had to wait for such an appointment. It has been conjectured that one of the reasons for Gödel's delayed promotion at the IAS was that he would not welcome the administrative work that would come with being a professor. There is some evidence for this from other sources, for in 1946 he wrote that he had not joined the main professional organization for logicians, the Association for Symbolic Logic, because committee or service work might be involved. There may have been other reasons for the delay. It could have been due to opposition from a colleague. There also seemed to be some apprehension about what would happen if Gödel were to take part in committee work. The worry was that he would only hinder efficient decision-making because of his legalistic sensibilities and penchant for over-analyzing issues. It is also plausible that concerns about his mental stability were involved in the delay in granting him a permanent position. John Dawson has suggested that when he was finally promoted as a permanent member, it was probably thanks to his old friend von Neumann.

Wartime Activities

In the Grandjean questionnaire, Gödel said he first studied the intuitionism of Brouwer in 1940, which is somewhat surprising. It seems that he would have read Brouwer earlier, given his excitement about Brouwer's lectures in Vienna. Soon after this, Gödel gave talks on some new work, "In What Sense is Intuitionistic Logic Constructive?" at Princeton and Yale. This material was not published during Gödel's lifetime. The typescript of the lecture was available in the Gödel literary estate around 1986 and appeared to be basically ready for publication, but it was not actually published until 1995, in *Kurt Gödel: Collected Works, Vol. III.*

The Gödels rented lodgings in Princeton until 1949, when they bought a house. Before this purchase, they had moved out of several apartments because Gödel complained of bad air from central heating. To Morgenstern, he frequently remarked about heating units emitting "smoke gases." On at least one occasion he had the heaters removed from the apartment, which made for a rather uncomfortable situation in the winter. At times he suspected that the refrigerator might be putting out some kind of poison gas. Meanwhile, Adele was a smoker. Some of Gödel's colleagues were quite alarmed by what seemed to be his paranoid behavior about his living conditions. One of them at the IAS contacted Gödel's doctor to try to determine whether there was any concern that Gödel might become violent and do some injury to himself or others. The doctor replied that he saw no imminent danger of such behavior.

It seems that Gödel probably gave up on trying to prove the independence of the CH around 1946, possibly a few years earlier. He had been working on this since around 1937, but he was not making a lot of headway. He began to spend more time on philosophy. From May 1941 to November 18, 1942, for example, he filled five of his philosophical notebooks.

There is a story about the Gödels' vacation trip to Blue Hill House in Maine in the summer of 1942. Gödel, as it happened, did not cease his work on the independence of CH while he was there. Quite the contrary. The manager of Blue Hill House at the time, a Mrs. Louise Frederick, remembered that Gödel was "unremittingly taciturn and dour" for the duration of his stay. He was a man "lost in thought." He spent most of the daylight hours in his room, where Adele did not permit the staff to enter. At night he took long walks, returning after midnight. He was clearly cogitating during these walks, according to Mrs. Frederick. Apparently, some of the neighbors became suspicious about his nocturnal wanderings. Here was this dour man with a thick German accent walking alone at night near the shore. Perhaps, they thought, he could be a spy, signaling to German ships or submarines in the bay.

In one of their apartments in Princeton, their neighbors were George and Bobbie Brown, who later recalled their interactions with the Gödels. According to the Browns, the Gödels were not very social. They noted that both Kurt and Adele had some odd behaviors. They said Kurt avoided leaving his apartment when certain foreign visitors came to town because he feared they might try to kill him. When the Gödels did invite the Browns to their apartment, they discovered that Kurt had insisted that the screens be left out of the windows so he could breathe properly. This meant their apartment was open to dust, drafts, and insects. Mrs. Brown recalled that Adele was extremely lonely, in part because there was no wartime communication between the U.S. and Austria. She was also "rueful that [she] had no child." When Mrs. Brown had a child, Adele "was most attentive and generous of her time and help."

John Dawson noted that Adele was nearly 40 at the time of her second marriage, and it is possible that she worried that a child might have mental problems. Kurt perhaps worried about the prevalence of cancer in Adele's family. It is not known whether Kurt wanted children. It seems that for him a child would have introduced uncertainty into the equation—something that would be out of his control. Adele confided in a friend that the Gödels had supported a foreign orphan during the war but balked at the opportunity to adopt the child later. Kurt evidently thought that only a blood relative should carry the Gödel name. Adele, it was reported, made children's dresses during the war to donate to relief efforts.

The Gödels did have pets. A cocker spaniel was hit by a car and killed after only about a year, but another dog named "Penny," which they got in 1953, lived a full life. They also had a pair of lovebirds. They evidently enjoyed their pets, which probably were especially salutary for Adele.

In 1942, the American philosopher Paul Schilpp invited Gödel to write a paper on Bertrand Russell's work in logic. Schilpp edited a famous series of books on philosophers and philosophically inclined scientists. The title of the book was *The Philosophy of Bertrand Russell.* Altogether, Schilpp would invite Gödel to contribute to volumes on four different figures. Each volume had the same format and was to include replies to the contributions, but Gödel's contribution to the Russell volume arrived late, and Russell declined to comment on it. Russell evidently had great respect for Gödel. The paper, which is quite interesting, was published in 1944. It is titled "Russell's Mathematical Logic" and covers various themes in Russell's work in this area. Gödel noted in the paper that Russell had at one time embraced realism (Platonism) about logic. He went on to express for the first time in a publication some of his own Platonistic views. Gödel said,

> Classes and concepts may, however, also be conceived as real objects, namely classes as "pluralities of things" or as structures consisting of a plurality of things and concepts as the properties and relations of things existing independently of our definitions and constructions . . . . It seems to me that the assumption of such objects is quite as legitimate as the assumption of physical bodies and there is quite as much reason to believe in their existence.

He was also studying Leibniz in 1944 and 1945. At the end of the Russell paper, he made a number of comments about Leibniz's project of developing the universal characteristic. Gödel claimed that our understanding of the foundations of mathematics might be improved if we do not give up hope about such a project. He was looking for a method that can help us to solve mathematical problems systematically. Later he would turn to Husserl with the same goal in mind.

Curiously, all of the books on and by Leibniz that were in Gödel's personal library have gone missing since they were deposited with his literary estate. The same is true for his books by Husserl.

What was Gödel seeking in Leibniz's writings? He was obviously interested in ideas about the universal characteristic and *calculus ratiocinator*, and he probably sought other insights into logical theory.

We also know that he liked aspects of Leibniz's monadology. He later said he hoped it could be developed into a comprehensive metaphysics with the help of Husserl's method. Gödel's ontological argument for the existence of God discussed below, was influenced by Leibniz's ideas. Leibniz's philosophy probably also appealed to him because of its unremitting rationalistic optimism. Leibniz, famously, is responsible for the claim that our world is the best of all possible worlds. This claim has, of course, been met with skepticism if not outright derision. Voltaire famously mocked the idea in his satirical novel *Candide*. Leibniz would not have had any problem agreeing that it *appears* that this is not the best of all possible worlds but he would have argued on theological-philosophical grounds that the *reality* is otherwise. In a similar vein, Gödel said "every chaos is a wrong appearance," that is, not real. Gödel was surrounded by chaos in Vienna and then during the war. In general, it is not difficult to find appearances of great evil in the world. Would it not offer consolation in dark times if one could actually believe that chaos was not real?

War is Over

Adele wished to visit Vienna immediately after the war. She learned that her father had died, and that three other family members had also died. Her mother was still living, but Adele worried about her care. The Gödels sent food, clothing and other staples to their families in the war's immediate aftermath. On Gödel's side, Marianne and Rudolf had survived, but some of his relatives had been forced to resettle in Germany. Kurt's godfather, Friedrich Redlich, had died in a Nazi gas chamber. Adele was not able to leave for Vienna until May 1947. She stayed there for seven months, visiting family and friends, taking care of her mother, and dealing with the apartment she and Kurt had left behind. In later years, Adele's absence for such a long period probably would have been intolerable for Kurt. Compared to Princeton, life in Europe was now very busy for her. While Adele was away, Morgenstern kept Gödel company, at least at first. After several months Morgenstern himself traveled to Vienna. Gödel was lonely during this period but dived into his work. Once Adele returned, the couple settled back into their usual routine. Kurt had lost weight during Adele's absence. His citizenship certificate in 1947 listed his weight as 110 pounds and height as five feet, seven inches. With Adele's return, he began to gain some weight and is reported to have looked much better.

There are records that Gödel had serious dietary problems in 1946. His brother reported that his chronic digestive troubles began around 1940. They had perhaps started even earlier. As a result, he was always underweight, never weighing more than 120 pounds. In 1946 he had persistent constipation, for which he constantly used laxatives. He began to keep a record of his laxative consumption and this continued for the next 30 years. It occupies five folders in his literary estate.

As Morgenstern got to know the Gödels better, his opinion of Adele did not improve. He said she was coarse and loud, displayed bad taste, monopolized conversation, and still spoke English very badly after ten years in America. Morgenstern allowed that she was a good cook, albeit in the heavy German style. Morgenstern's wife was disturbed on at least one occasion by the way Adele spoke to Kurt and, in her view, terrorized him. Others also spoke of Adele as sharp-tongued and strong-willed, rude and irascible. Even Gödel said that at times she displayed symptoms of clinical hysteria and often formed "quite wrong impressions" of other people. She would imagine that there was enmity toward her when none existed. She may have bullied Kurt and made demands on him that kept him from his work. Still, there are good reasons to believe that, without her, he would have been much worse off. Gödel did not have much interest in social events anyway.

Gödel gave an important lecture at the Princeton University Bicentennial in 1946, but it was published for the first time only in 1965. As noted earlier, Gödel believed that we had finally arrived at an "absolute" concept of computability with Turing's analysis of the notion. Various alternative characterizations of the concept of computability had turned out to be provably equivalent. We have just one exact concept of computability, whereas we know that formal proof is always relative to the formal system in which it is defined. We have to "diagonalize" out of a given system to formally prove more and more mathematical theorems, but we do not have to diagonalize out of the concept of computability to find more and more of what is computable. In the Princeton lecture, on the analogy with absolute computability, Gödel suggested that there might also be absolute concepts of provability and definability. These ideas led to the development of extensive lines of research.

During 1946–47, Gödel was invited to write a paper on Cantor's continuum problem for the *American Mathematical Monthly* and another paper for a collection on Einstein. The paper on Cantor's continuum problem, which originally appeared in 1947 and then in a revised and extended form in 1964, was destined to become one of Gödel's most quoted publications. The 1964 version included more philosophical material on Platonism and mathematical intuition. We will come back to it in Chapter 12.

Around the time he would have been preparing the Einstein paper, Gödel wrote that he had not been able to stop thinking about his work. "Even in a cinema or with a radio I could only listen with half an ear . . . I have now settled the matter to such an extent that I can again sleep peacefully." These comments probably give some insight into his work habits.

10

Einstein, Physics and Time

Gödel and Einstein met in the fall of 1933 when they were both in Princeton for the first time. Gödel had made several trips to the United States during the '30s, but their friendship began in 1942 after Gödel had moved to America permanently. They became close friends. It is said they talked to each other almost daily from that time until Einstein's death in 1955.

The Einstein-Gödel Friendship

In 1965, Oskar Morgenstern wrote, "Einstein told me that in the late years of his life he has continually sought Gödel's company, in order to have discussions with him. Once he said to me that his own work no longer meant much, that he came to the Institute merely to have the privilege to walk home with Gödel." On his side, Gödel wrote to his mother that Einstein was the "personification of friendliness." John Dawson has observed that Einstein was, in fact, one of Gödel's protectors. There is no record of the content of their conversations, but they apparently spoke primarily about philosophy, physics, and politics. If only we had some way of overhearing these two in conversation! Gödel's own explanation of why Einstein liked to converse with him was that he frequently held an opinion contrary to Einstein's and made no attempt to conceal his disagreement. In particular, he said he had always been very skeptical about the idea of a unified field theory. Hao Wang speculated that an important reason for their friendship was the feeling of equality between the two, their shared clarity of thought, and the attractiveness and novelty of Gödel's ideas and how he expressed them. Although they disagreed on certain issues, they also had some things in common. Both had found themselves choosing between mathematics and physics when they were younger. Both rejected the idea of indeterminacy in physics and thought that quantum mechanics did not provide a complete description of physical reality. By outward appearance, neither was as productive during this period, although it turned out that Gödel had suppressed some very interesting work.

There are many stories about Gödel and Einstein. It is known that they frequently walked to and from the Institute together and that they visited one another's homes. One of Einstein's assistants, Ernst Gabor Straus (1922-1986), related that "No story of Einstein in Princeton would be complete without mentioning his really warm and very close friendship with Kurt Gödel. They were very, very dissimilar people, but for some reason, they understood each other very well and appreciated each other enormously." Straus said Gödel was certainly by far Einstein's best friend in Einstein's later years. He said Einstein was gregarious and full of laughter and common sense, while Gödel was extremely solemn, very serious, quite solitary, and distrustful of common sense as a means of arriving at the truth. Both men, Straus said, shared the fundamental quality of going directly and wholeheartedly to questions at the very center of things. Einstein knew at a certain point that he did not have long to live, but he had revealed this to hardly anyone and not to Gödel. When he died on April 18, 1955, at the age of 76, Gödel was greatly shocked. He missed his dear friend very much.

One of the stories always told about Gödel and Einstein concerns the occasion on which Gödel was to attend his U.S. citizenship hearing in April 1948. Einstein and Morgenstern were to be his witnesses. To take the routine citizenship examination, Gödel had seriously studied the U.S. Constitution. On the day before the examination, Gödel came to Morgenstern in an excited state, saying that he had discovered a logical-legal possibility by virtue of which the United States could be transformed into a dictatorship. Morgenstern urged Gödel to keep quiet about his discovery at the examination, whatever his argument's logical merits might be. Morgenstern drove Einstein and Gödel to the examination the next morning. Along the way, Einstein kept telling amusing anecdotes one after the other to distract Gödel. This was apparently successful, except that when they arrived for the examination, Einstein and Morgenstern were worried. The official presiding over the event began by addressing Gödel, "Up to now you have held German citizenship." Gödel corrected him, explaining that he held Austrian citizenship. The official continued: "Anyhow, it was under an evil dictatorship . . . but fortunately that is not possible in America." Gödel cried out that, on the contrary, "I know how that can happen." Einstein, Morgenstern and the official all had great trouble restraining Gödel from elaborating on his discovery so that the proceedings could be brought to a close. Gödel was successful in his bid for U.S. citizenship, but it has never been revealed what he thought the problem was. Had he found a contradiction in the Constitution? One can only speculate, but perhaps there is some indication in the untranscribed notes in his literary estate.

Relativity Theory, Time Travel, and the Illusion of Time

When Gödel turned to physics in the late 1940s, he produced a series of very interesting technical and philosophical papers. Their topics included novel solutions to the field equations of general relativity theory, the possibility of time travel, the philosophy of time, and idealism and Kant. Some of these papers he published and some not. According to Gödel, his work on relativity theory did not spring from his discussions with Einstein but was instead motivated by his own interests in Kant's views on time and idealism. Idealism about time is the view that time is mind-dependent or due to our own cognitive structure. If time is relative to human subjectivity, then there might even be beings for whom there is no experience of time, change or temporal passage. Gödel noted that Kant mentions this in his *Critique of Pure Reason* (B54) where it is said that for beings with forms of cognition other than ours, "those modifications which we represent to ourselves as changes would give rise to a perception in which the idea of time, and therefore also of change, would not occur at all."

In his first publication in this area, in 1949, Gödel presented a solution to the Einstein field equations of general relativity theory in which the universe is rotating and not expanding but is the same at all points of space and time, and in which it is possible to travel into the past. Gödel was the first to consider models in which the universe is rotating, and he also provided the first solution in which it was possible to travel into the past. This solution naturally generated a lot of discussion, which has not abated to this day. Apart from the remarkable possibility of time travel to the past, it led to vexed questions about the relationship between general relativity theory and the concept of causality. What could it now mean to say that earlier events cause later events? (Gödel evidently believed in strict causality in physics.) In another technical paper from 1952, Gödel presented rotating cosmological models that are expanding but that do not have the possibility of travel into the past. The 1949 technical paper was quickly followed up with a short paper on the more philosophical aspects of his time travel solution. He contributed this to the special volume on the work of Einstein that was edited by Paul Schilpp.

Einstein, of course, revolutionized our views on time in physics. When learning the theory of relativity, it is still common for people to find its account of time and space stunning. Relativity theory replaces Newton's concept of "absolute" time with a relative conception, so the time of events in the external world is relative to the observer or frame of reference. There is no objective "now" point on which all observers might agree. According to special relativity, an observer $O1$ in one reference frame might regard two events A, B as occurring simultaneously while an observer $O2$ in another reference frame moving relative to $O1$ might regard event B as occurring before event A, and a third observer $O3$ might regard B as occurring after A. $O1$, $O2$, and $O3$ do not agree on what is occurring now. For $O2$, for example, B is in the past when A occurs. Generally, observers in different reference frames will not agree on what is past, present or future. This will now be relative to reference frame or, as we might also say, coordinate system. We cannot speak about an objective 'now' point as we can on an absolute view of time.

In connection with the special theory of relativity, it was argued early on that the relativity of simultaneity implied that time is an illusion. In that view, time is not objectively real. As Gödel noted, special relativity seems to offer proof for the views of philosophers such as Parmenides and Kant, and modern idealists such as J.E.M. McTaggart, who deny the objectivity of change. They consider change to be an illusion or an appearance due to our special mode of perception. The sense of the passage of time is due entirely to our own subjective constitution. In a comment occasioned by the death of his old friend Michele Besso, for example, Einstein said,

> Now Besso has departed from this strange world a little ahead of me. That means nothing. People like us, who believe in physics, know that the distinction between past, present and future is only a stubbornly persistent illusion.

Science has a history of showing us how what we took to be true of the world was, in fact, an illusion. But could the same thing be true of time? This seems really radical. It raises deep questions about the relationship of science to common sense. What is the relationship of what the philosopher Wilfrid Sellars calls the "manifest image" of the world to the "scientific image" of the world? Husserl probed this issue even more deeply in his writings on the differences between the everyday human "lifeworld" and mathematized natural science.

Gödel did not rest content with arguments from the special theory of relativity. He proceeded directly to the general theory and the field equations. On the basis of the solutions known when he was writing, it appeared that in general relativity, where we take account of gravity and the motion of matter, there could still exist something like absolute time. The British physicist James Jeans had put forward a view like this. Gödel said he wanted to see whether this was a necessary property of all possible solutions, and he then discovered through his technical work that it was not.

Gödel pointed out that in his time-travel model, velocities near the speed of light would be required to travel to the past. He even offered some calculations about the weight of the "fuel" that would be required for a rocket ship to travel to the past. This model includes closed time-like loops. Time can loop back around on itself. It is often argued that space-time in relativity theory presents us with a "block" view of the universe in which time is "spatialized." Thus, one can almost picture the closed time-like loops as one would in a diagram of a spatial region. In space-time, everything that for us constitutes the past, present, and future is given as a frozen block. The entire collection of events that is successive for us is just represented for a material particle by a line, the particle's world-line.

Gödel was certainly aware of the paradoxes associated with time travel to the past, such as the "grandfather paradox." The time traveler could go back to the past and kill his grandfather, but then who would have killed the grandfather? In the face of such contradictions, Gödel's response was that it was probably not actually feasible to journey to one's past. It might be a practical impossibility to reach the velocities necessary to complete the voyage in a reasonable time, and yet he said it cannot be excluded *a priori* that the real world's space-time structure is of the type described in the model. While this may be true, it is known that Gödel's time travel model yields no red shift for distant objects in the universe, whereas such red shift is actually observed in nature. So the model does not seem to square with how nature actually is. Among other things, this just shows us how much the true nature of the cosmos is underdetermined by solutions to the field equations. Out of the many possible worlds allowed by the equations of the general theory of relativity, which is the actual world? There are many solutions to the equations, but we have to combine the mathematics with observation to develop a sense of what the universe is really like.

Gödel said the inference to the non-objectivity of change at least applies in the rotating universes that allow for time travel. He argued that the possibility of time travel, of closed time-like loops, further strengthens the idealistic viewpoint. If one could travel into the past in such worlds, then to assume an objective lapse of time would lose every justification in such worlds. That is because in whatever way we assume time to be lapsing, there will always exist possible observers to whose experienced lapse of time there is no corresponding objective lapse of time. If the experience of the lapse of time can exist without an objective lapse of time, then no reason can be given for why an objective lapse of time should be assumed at all.

If such conditions prevail in certain *possible* worlds, does this have any real meaning for whether an objective lapse of time exists in *our* world? Gödel said yes, for two reasons. First, there also exist *expanding* rotating solutions and in such universes, absolute time might also fail to exist, and it is not impossible that our world is a universe of this kind. The second reason concerns the compatibility with the laws of nature of worlds in which there is no distinguished absolute time, and therefore in which no objective lapse of time can exist. That compatibility throws light on the meaning of time, also in those worlds in which an absolute time can be defined. If someone asserts that absolute time is lapsing, then he accepts the consequence that whether or not an objective lapse of time exists depends on the particular way in which matter and its motion are arranged in the world. This is not a flat contradiction, but it is an unsatisfactory philosophical view. Why? Presumably, an objective lapse of time should be founded on the laws of nature and should not depend on the special contingent manner in which matter and its motion are distributed in the world.

Gödel published his technical results on rotating universes in exact, tightly constructed, highly technical papers that seemed almost to come from nowhere. In fact, a philosophical backstory led to these results. He told us how he arrived at his solutions for rotating universes. He said he was working on the similarity between Kant and relativity theory insofar as both theories deny the objective existence of time in the Newtonian sense. As mentioned above, on the cosmological solutions known when he was writing, there could exist something like an absolute time, but he wanted to see whether this is a necessary property of all possible cosmological solutions. He then discovered through his technical work that it is not. It is very interesting that it was again Gödel's philosophical interests that led him to deep technical work, this time in physics. This friendliness toward philosophy contrasts sharply with some physicists' derisive comments about philosophy. It shows, I think, that philosophy is not vapid and no longer of use to physicists. It is difficult to say what kinds of fruitful ideas and developments might come out of the interactions of these disciplines.

Gödel clearly had an interest in observational data and not only theory in his work in cosmology. In Gödel's literary estate are two notebooks devoted to calculations of galaxies' angular orientations. Gödel hoped they might display a preferred direction that would help to support his views.

Additional Ideas about Time

Before we leave the subject, several additional points about Gödel's interest in time are worth mentioning. First, Gödel was a Platonist about logic and mathematics, at least in the later part of his career. He held that the sciences of logic and mathematics are concerned with abstract, acausal, non-spatial concepts, and with objects that are unchanging and timeless or "eternal." He argued for an eternal, timeless, and fixed objective mathematical and logical reality, in part on the basis of his incompleteness theorems. Interestingly, he reached the conclusion that the objective physical world is also timeless, but now this was based on his work on relativity theory and Kant. Hao Wang remarked, correctly I think, that

> On the whole, Gödel seems to favor the fundamental perspective of seeing objective reality, both the physical and the conceptual, as eternal, timeless, and fixed.

A second point is that Gödel recognized a distinction between inner and outer time.

He was very interested in Husserl's work on the phenomenology of inner time. He had read Husserl's published lectures on this topic, thought of them as foundational for philosophy, and discussed some of the ideas with Wang. Although there is no space here to consider his comments on time and subjectivity, it is worth mentioning these because they round out Gödel's views on time and because his literary estate may contain additional interesting materials on this.

Finally, Gödel admitted that, in the present imperfect state of physics, it cannot be maintained with certainty that the space-time scheme of relativity theory really describes the material world's objective structure. Perhaps it should be considered only one step beyond the appearances, and toward the things, that is, as one *level of objectification* to be followed by others. Gödel said quantum physics, in particular, seems to indicate that physical reality is something even further from the appearances than the four-dimensional Einstein-Minkowski world. Gödel also cited the famous Einstein, Podolsky, and Rosen paper at one point and endorsed the idea that quantum mechanics does not give us a complete description of the physical world. With Einstein, he shared the view that quantum mechanics is incomplete. It is known that there are remarks on quantum mechanics in Gödel's philosophical notebooks but, to date, these have not been transcribed from his Gabelsberger shorthand.

It should be kept in mind that all of Gödel's publications about time are built around the theory of relativity. It is still unclear how relativity theory is to be combined with quantum mechanics, and the two theories appear to have conflicting views on time. Some physicists think efforts to unify these fundamental theories of nature will call for major changes in our view of time. It is difficult to say what physics will tell us about time a hundred years from now.

11

Settled in Princeton

In 1949, the Gödels bought a house in Princeton. Adele was finally very pleased to have a place of her own. At the time they purchased it, Kurt thought it was too expensive and that they might have trouble keeping it. This fear proved to be unfounded, and they lived in the house for the rest of their lives. Adele made a host of improvements over the years and enlisted Kurt's help with some of her plans. When she placed a pink flamingo lawn ornament in their yard, Kurt pronounced it "awfully charming."

Research, Honors and Life

Gödel and Morgenstern made an effort in 1949 to have Leibniz's manuscripts in Hanover microfilmed for the Princeton University library. As Morgenstern began to look into the matter, he ran into difficulties. There was supposed to be one copy of the critical catalog of the Interacademy edition of Leibniz's manuscripts in the United States, supposedly deposited with the National Academy of Sciences, but Morgenstern was told it could not be found. It also could not be found at either the Library of Congress or the Smithsonian Institution. The catalog's disappearance was never explained. This only served to fuel Gödel's conspiracy theories. When Gödel and Morgenstern approached the archive in Hanover directly, they ran into complications with funding the project. Meanwhile, another effort of the same type by Professor Paul Schrecker at the University of Pennsylvania was under way and was evidently more advanced. Schrecker eventually succeeded in having a copy of the Leibniz materials deposited in the library at the University of Pennsylvania, but it is not known whether Gödel ever used it.

Two years later, Gödel developed a bleeding duodenal ulcer, which he delayed treating for so long that he finally required blood transfusions. The condition was life-threatening, and Gödel's survival was in doubt for several days. His brother Rudolf said that afterward, Kurt lived on such a strict diet that he lost even more weight and was continually under-nourished. Nonetheless, when Kurt recovered and returned home, his depression about his condition subsided. Adele once again took care of him. It was around this time that Gödel received the prestigious Einstein Award. He had been invited to present endowed lectures on earlier occasions, but this was the first academic honor bestowed upon him. At the award ceremony, with Einstein prominently in attendance, John von Neumann presented the medal to Gödel, with the words that his work in logic would be "a landmark which will remain visible far in space and time."

He planned to visit his mother in Europe in the fall of 1951 but did not go through with the journey. He said it would be necessary for him to maintain his strict diet were he to travel to Vienna, and wrote to his mother and brother that he lived principally on butter, about a quarter pound a day. This he supplemented with some eggs, milk, puréed potatoes, and baby food. Gödel would use issues about his diet and some other odd reasons in always declining to return to Austria. Adele would travel to Europe and elsewhere with some frequency, but Kurt could not bring himself to leave Princeton for anything other than short trips within the United States.

He did travel to Providence, Rhode Island, in 1951 to present an important lecture to the American Mathematical Society on the implications of his incompleteness theorems. This is known as the Gibbs Lecture, and it was only published in 1995, in one of the volumes of his *Collected Works*. It is very interesting for its discussions of the inexhaustibility of mathematics, minds and machines, the question whether there are absolutely undecidable problems, and Platonism.

In addition to the Einstein Award, Gödel received an honorary Doctor of Letters (Litt.D.) from Yale University in 1951. An honorary Doctor of Science (Sc.D.) from Harvard followed in 1952. Gödel traveled to Cambridge, Mass. to receive the honorary degree at Harvard and Adele accompanied him on this occasion. It was unusual for her to attend academic events with her husband but she enjoyed the visit very much. She was impressed favorably by the people she met there and by the university's location. Unlike the small town of Princeton, greater Boston was a metropolis with resources and demographics she could appreciate. Kurt evidently had the opportunity to take a position at Harvard but declined. He was very pleased with the citation that accompanied the honorary degree, which spoke of him as "the discoverer of the most significant mathematical truth of this century."

Good news soon arrived on several other fronts. He was elected to the National Academy of Sciences in 1953 and was also promoted, finally, to professor at the IAS. On the occasion of his promotion, Gödel wrote to his mother that he would not have any lecturing duties and yet his salary would be higher than salaries at Princeton University. He told Wang that, with his appointment, his work was now split in three ways: Institute work, mathematics, and philosophy. There are reports that he became keenly interested in the Institute's affairs. Hassler Whitney, one of his colleagues, said that after Gödel's promotion it was hard to appoint new visiting members in logic since Gödel could not "prove to himself that a number of candidates shouldn't be members, with the evidence at hand."

His old colleague from Vienna, Rudolf Carnap, visited the IAS from 1952 to 1954 but there seems to be no information about his interaction with Gödel at this time. Carnap's *Intellectual Biography* does include some pages on his visit but, oddly, makes no mention of Gödel. In 1953, Schilpp had invited Gödel to contribute a paper to another book in his series, this time on Carnap. As mentioned in Chapter 6, Gödel drafted six versions of the paper, titled "Is Mathematics Syntax of Language?" but in the end never contributed a paper to the volume. All six versions of the paper are preserved in the Gödel literary estate, all basically ready for publication. Two versions were published in 1995 in *Kurt Gödel: Collected Works*. Other versions have been published elsewhere. The reasons he gave for not contributing a paper were that he was not satisfied with the result, that the paper was very critical of Carnap's position, and that it would be unfair to publish the paper since it was too late for Carnap to reply. Later he told

Wang that he thought the paper definitively refuted Carnap's idea that mathematics was syntax of language but that he did not want to publish it because it did not offer a satisfactory philosophical alternative to Carnap's position. The satisfactory alternative would have been some rigorous type of Platonic rationalism. The paper's various versions are quite interesting, and they do contain powerful arguments against the position Carnap held at the time of his book, *The Logical Syntax of Language*. Gödel worked on the drafts from 1953 until 1958.

Altogether, Schilpp had invited Gödel to write papers for four different volumes. Only in the case of the Einstein volume did Gödel contribute a paper for which a reply was published. The Russell paper was published but without a reply by Russell, and the Carnap paper was written in six versions but not published in Gödel's lifetime. Gödel was also invited to write on the philosopher of science Karl Popper but this he declined outright.

Politics and Other Events in the 1950s

During the 1950s, Gödel became more attentive to politics. He wrote to his mother in 1952 that his focus on politics for two months had left him with little time for anything else. In 1953, he said "We live in a world in which 99% of all beautiful things are destroyed in the bud," and that certain forces were at work that were "directly submerging the good." This focus on politics was quite unlike the Vienna years. Gödel became disillusioned with his adopted country during the McCarthy era. The head of the IAS, the famous physicist Robert Oppenheimer, was under surveillance by the FBI, and so was Einstein. The FBI director, J. Edgar Hoover, was notorious for abusing his power, among other things, by staging witch-hunts for alleged Communists. Gödel's bouts of paranoia could not have been helped by these conditions, which may even have exacerbated them. To Marianne and Rudolf, he expressed opinions about a number of the era's political events. In the presidential race between Adlai Stevenson and Dwight Eisenhower, Gödel voted for Eisenhower. Einstein quipped to one of his colleagues, "You know, Gödel has really gone completely crazy—he voted for Eisenhower!"

From letters to his mother and brother during this period, we also learn about some of his other non-academic interests. For example, he said he enjoyed reading, attending opera and visiting museums in New York, and watching plays or variety programs on television. He said he did some calisthenics and swam in the ocean. He played a game called Skee-ball on the boardwalk at the New Jersey shore and reported that he developed some skill at it. He discussed German literature and remarked that he was not favorably disposed toward most of Goethe's work. He found Shakespeare "hard to get into." He mentioned his recent discovery of the work of Franz Kafka. He also wrote to his mother and brother about some issues in history, and to his mother about religion.

Adele took a second trip to Vienna in early 1953, and then another in 1955. Gödel planned to visit his mother in the summer of 1955 but did not go, explaining that his doctor had advised against going in the summer. Some points of contention that emerged in the correspondence with his mother concerned his reasons for failing to return to Vienna, issues about his diet, and defending Adele. Marianne was quite critical of Adele. She thought Adele should not leave Kurt alone while she visited Vienna, and that she was spending too much money on her trips. Gödel conceded that his wife had "great faults" but said Adele was in general quite normal "as far as life in Princeton is concerned."

Some of Adele's observations about the IAS were amusing. According to the logician Georg Kreisel, "On one occasion she painted the IAS, which she usually called 'the home of old-age pensioners,' as teeming with pretty girl students who queued up at the office doors of permanent professors." She also referred to Kurt, affectionately, as a "*strammer Bursche*," which means something like "a strapping lad." In 1956, at age eighty-eight, Adele's mother was having serious health problems, and Adele brought her back to share the Gödels' home in Princeton. She lived with them until she died of heart disease in March 1959. Adele went on a vacation for three and a half weeks that summer and Kurt stayed behind and worked. In the late autumn, she went to Vienna again for about two months.

Alan Turing had died in 1954, evidently of suicide by eating an apple slice that had been dipped in cyanide. When Turing's suicide was mentioned, Gödel asked whether Turing was married. Told that he was not, Gödel said, "Maybe he wanted to get married but could not." Turing was homosexual, presumably unbeknownst to Gödel, and was in fact prosecuted for having had a relationship with a man. This was illegal at the time in England, and Turing could have been jailed for up to two years. The alternative punishment was to be treated for a year with hormone injections that were supposed to correct his "problem." The hormone that was administered was estrogen, which had the effect of causing him to grow breasts. There has been a lot of speculation about what led Turing to take his own life. Turing had worked on code breaking during the war and was privy to some top-secret information. He had done much to help his country and the Allies.

Gödel was honored again in 1957 with election to the American Academy of Arts and Sciences. But another person who was very important to Gödel, John von Neumann, died in 1957. Von Neumann was a remarkable theoretician who was also at home in practical applications of mathematics and computer science. He had worked on the design of the EDVAC and other computers and as an advisor to military and governmental agencies, including work on the Manhattan Project. Like Turing, von Neumann had become very interested in actually building computers. Gödel, however, never showed much interest in pursuing practical applications of computability theory. In his last letter to von Neumann, Gödel had discussed some mathematical issues. In it, he formulated what is believed to be the first statement of what is now known as the "P = NP problem" in computability theory. Von Neumann was too ill to respond. The P = NP problem is still generally regarded as the most important open problem in computability theory.

An incident at this time clearly displayed Gödel's caution about how his work was perceived. The well-known philosopher of science at Columbia University, Ernest Nagel (1901-1985), wrote to Gödel to inquire about including his incompleteness paper and a related paper from 1934 as appendices in a book he was to co-author with James Newman (1907-1966). The book would explain these results to a popular audience. Nagel and Newman also wanted to indicate the logical and philosophical implications of Gödel's theorems. Gödel had a number of reservations about this and, in particular, was not happy with their presentation of the theorems' philosophical implications. The episode is chronicled in correspondence between Nagel and Gödel. In the end, they could not reach an agreement, and the papers did not appear in what became *Gödel's Proof*, a successful book that is still in print.

Gödel's mother and brother visited Kurt in Princeton for the first time in 1958. They had never been to the United States, and Gödel had not seen them since 1940. In 1960, Gödel's mother and brother were in the country again for a stay of several months. Adele went to Vienna in November and returned in December. Gödel said in a letter that during Adele's 1960 trip he ate mostly eggs.

During Rudolf and Marianne's second visit, Gödel looked unwell and undernourished, according to Morgenstern. Kurt had been making weekly visits to a psychiatrist, but his anorexia continued unabated as did his fixation on his bowel habits. He would set the alarm on his wristwatch to remind him when to take certain pills, and he carried around a box of baking soda for his digestive problems. When his mother returned to Vienna, Gödel wrote to tell her he would soon try the enema tubes she had given him. He thought the milk of magnesia he was taking on an empty stomach would help. Gödel was chronically malnourished at this time, but it is not clear that his condition was worse than usual. It had been reported for some time that Gödel preferred hot weather. He was often seen in Princeton bundled up in an overcoat even on warm days. His sensitivity to the cold was perhaps related to the fact that he was very thin and had an unhealthy diet. Despite Kurt's complaints about air quality, Adele continued to smoke in their home.

Gödel's mother and brother visited Princeton again in the autumn of 1962. Adele had continued to travel, taking trips in 1959, 1960, 1961, and 1963. She vacationed at the seaside for about a month in the summer of 1964, and took an extended summer vacation and "cure" in Europe in 1966.

Rudolf said he did not understand why Kurt never returned to Vienna after the war. He always had an excuse, usually not very convincing to Rudolf. He did appreciate Kurt's invitations for him and his mother to visit Princeton and said they spent many happy hours with his brother and Adele while there. Gödel's regular correspondence with his mother had resumed after the war, and this lasted until her death in 1966.

Gödel's last publication, his so-called *Dialectica* paper, appeared in 1958. He had been working on the paper for a long time but could not let it go. It was published in a volume honoring his old friend Paul Bernays. Even after it appeared in print, he could not stop revising it. In this paper, he extended constructive reasoning beyond finitism and argued that the resulting system was more evident than that provided by intuitionism. On the basis of this work, it was possible to provide a consistency proof for Peano arithmetic. By the second incompleteness theorem, this would not, of course, be possible in Peano arithmetic itself. The paper is quite interesting and led to many developments and extensions.

The Turn to Husserl

Gödel began to study Husserl's philosophy in 1959. Gödel told Wang that his Carnap paper(s) refuted the claim that mathematics is syntax of language but said little about what mathematics is. Wang added, "At the time he probably felt that Husserl's work promised to yield convincing reasons for his own beliefs about what mathematics is." Gödel was interested almost exclusively in the work that Husserl did after 1907. That was the year Husserl began to develop what he called transcendental eidetic phenomenology, which he came to associate in some ways, after Leibniz, with a monadology. According to Wang, Gödel said that at one time he thought philosophy could be pursued in the same manner as science, or at least by reflecting on science, but then he decided later that philosophy needs a different method, such as that proposed by Husserl. Gödel said, "What Husserl has done [is] . . . to teach . . . an attitude of mind which enables one to direct the attention rightly . . . ." Wang reported that Gödel wished to use Husserl's method "to arrive at a system of metaphysics that would be of comparable scope with Leibniz's monadology but more solidly founded on a shareable and disciplined intuition."

Two years later, he prepared a very interesting text in which he discussed his incompleteness theorems in relation to Husserl's philosophy. The text was evidently intended to be a lecture that marked the occasion of his election to the American Philosophical Society, but it became known only much later. It was written in Gabelsberger shorthand and was transcribed and then published only in 1995. It appears in Volume III of *Kurt Gödel: Collected Works*. In this paper, Gödel arranged philosophical worldviews according to their degree and manner of affinity to metaphysics. He pictured positions along a line with skepticism, materialism, and positivism on one side (the left) and spiritualism, idealism, and theology on the right. In this schema, empiricism belongs on the left, while rationalism and *a priorism* belong on the right. Gödel said the development of philosophy since the Renaissance has, on the whole, moved from the right to the left, and that this trend has also made itself felt in mathematics, even though mathematicians traditionally have inclined toward rightward positions. In this schema, Carnap's view of mathematics as syntax of language would certainly be on the left side. Gödel's view of Hilbert's program is very interesting. He said Hilbert tried to combine the two tendencies but in a way that is impossible. From the rightward side Hilbert's program wants to keep the ideas that there are no absolutely unsolvable problems in mathematics and that proofs of propositions should provide a secure grounding for the propositions. The problem with Hilbert's program, Gödel said, is that it translates these rightward features into demands on axiomatic formal systems, which are supposed to be concrete, given in sense perception, finitary, and so on. These latter characteristics all accord with the leftward *Zeitgeist* that has been developing since the Renaissance.

Gödel argued that the incompleteness theorems then enter the picture and show why Hilbert's formalism will not work. Hilbert's attempted combination is too strongly oriented toward the left, and the incompleteness theorems refute it. We need a new combination if we are to do justice to the two rightward features Hilbert wanted to preserve. He thought that for this we should turn to Husserl's transcendental eidetic philosophy, which offers a more suitable view of meaning clarification. What we need to do is to clarify and extend our knowledge of abstract concepts. Husserl has a methodology that should help us with this without just plunging us into another untenable rightward metaphysics. Gödel also said he thought Husserl's view does justice for the first time to the core of Kant's transcendental philosophy. We can add that in doing so, it also speaks to the main problems that Gödel always had with some of Kant's ideas. Kant's views on mathematics are already skewed too far to the left, he believed. One sees this, for example, in Kant's narrow conception of intuition as comprising only sensory intuition and in his reduced view of reason.

12

Later Years

I n the 1960s and '70s, Gödel continued to produce interesting work, remarkably, amidst periods of very serious illness. He also continued to receive honors for his achievements, especially the incompleteness theorems. His last days were fraught with depression, paranoia, and other difficulties. Adele, who had helped him so much on other occasions, was not able to assist him due to her own serious health problems.

"My Philosophical Viewpoint"
In the 1960s, Gödel worked mostly on philosophy and had returned to the continuum problem. He said his health was exceptionally poor in 1961, but he did not elaborate on why this was so. Sometime around 1960, he had made a list titled "My philosophical viewpoint." Written in Gabelsberger shorthand, it was found in a bundle of papers in his literary estate. The most recent corrected transcription and English translation by Eva-Maria Engelen reads,

> 1. The world is rational.
> 2. Human reason can, in principle, be developed more highly (through certain techniques).
> 3. There are systematic methods for the solution of all problems (also in art, etc.)
> 4. There are other worlds and rational beings, who are of the other and higher kind.
> 5. The world in which we now live is not the only one in which we live or have lived.
> 6. Incomparably more is knowable *a priori* than is currently known.

7. The development of human thought since the Renaissance is thoroughly one-sided.

8. Reason in mankind will be developed on every side.

9. The formally correct is a science of reality.

10. Materialism is false.

11. The higher beings are connected to the other beings by analogy, not by composition.

12. Concepts have an objective existence (likewise mathematical theorems).

13. There is a scientific (exact) philosophy {and theology}, (this is also most fruitful for science) which deals with the concepts of the highest abstractness.

14. Religions are, for the most part, bad, but Religion is not.

Some of these ideas we have seen above, and there is little reason to believe that he later rejected them. His notebooks may shed further light on them and especially on items 4, 5, 9, and 11. Some of the items, such as 1, 2, 3, 4, 6, 10, 11 and 13, are clearly aligned with Leibniz. This may also include items 5, 9, and 12. Some items were clearly influenced by Husserl, such as 2, 6, 7, 8, 12, 13 (except for theology), and maybe 1 and 10. There are also hints of Plato, as in items 2, 5, 6, 10, 12, and maybe some others. Gödel's statements here are terse.

It looked like the incident with Nagel and Newman was going to repeat itself when the philosophers Paul Benacerraf and Hilary Putnam (1926-2016) proposed in 1963 to publish two of Gödel's papers in a collection they were editing on the philosophy of mathematics. They wanted to reprint the paper "Russell's Mathematical Logic" and a revised edition of "What is Cantor's Continuum Problem?" Gödel was reluctant because he thought they were not sympathetic to his philosophical views. He feared that they might make negative comments in their introduction to the volume. After they had assured him that they had no intention of evaluating his papers, Gödel allowed them to be published in what has become a classic, *Philosophy of Mathematics: Selected Readings*.

The 1964 version of "What is Cantor's Continuum Problem?" in the Benacerraf and Putnam volume contained a new philosophical supplement in which Gödel expressed his platonic rationalism, the objects of transfinite set theory . . . clearly do not belong to the physical world . . . . But despite their remoteness from sense experience, we do have something like a perception also of the objects of set theory, as is seen from the fact that the axioms force themselves upon us as being true. I don't see any reason why we should have less confidence in this kind of perception, i.e., in mathematical intuition, than in sense perception, which induces us to build up physical theories and to expect that future sense perceptions will agree with them, and, moreover, to believe that a question not decidable now has meaning and may be decided in the future. The set-theoretical paradoxes are hardly any more troublesome for mathematics than deceptions of the senses are for physics. That new mathematical intuitions leading to a decision of such problems as Cantor's continuum problem are perfectly possible was pointed out earlier.

He then included further comments about the idea of mathematical intuition and about the analogy between mathematical intuition and sense perception. It is clear from his literary estate that he had some of Husserl's ideas in mind when he wrote this supplement. There have been many interpretations of the passages on intuition, most of which have shown no awareness of the fact that at the time he was studying and influenced by Husserl's work.

The comments in this passage on the paradoxes are also interesting, and he had more to say about this in some other writings. For example, he mentioned to Wang how paradoxes might arise from mixing two or more exact concepts in one intuitive concept. With the right kind of meaning clarification, we should be able to remove paradoxes. There is again an analogy with sense perception: we cannot distinguish two neighboring stars a long distance away, but with a telescope, we see that there are indeed two stars.

More Honors and More Health Problems
Throughout the 1960s, Gödel received numerous invitations to participate in conferences and to honor his 60th birthday in 1966, but

he always declined on the grounds that his health was too poor. That year, he refused an honorary professorship at the University of Vienna and also membership in the Austrian Academy of Sciences. He also refused to take part in the attempt to award him a national medal for art and science in Austria. On the other hand, he did not object in 1967 when he was made an honorary member of the London Mathematical Society, or in 1968 when the Royal Society in the United Kingdom elected him a foreign member, or when he became a corresponding member of the Institut de France in 1972. Gödel was being showered with recognition, but a pattern here suggests he could not bring himself to accept honors from Austria. In 1967, he was also awarded an honorary Doctor of Science (Sc.D.) degree from Amherst College.

Marianne and Rudolf visited the Gödels again in May of 1964. Soon after her visit, Marianne began to have some serious health problems. At one point, she was diagnosed with angina. Kurt was concerned about her condition and tried to convince her that the angina was actually a nervous affliction. He told her he had been taking nitroglycerin for some time. He arranged to share the cost of her medical treatment with Rudolf, but he did not consider going to see her. Marianne had wanted to be with Kurt on his 60th birthday in 1966 and was very disappointed that she could not make the trip. She telephoned on his birthday, April 28. Two months later, in July 1966, Gödel's mother died in Vienna. She had lived to the age of 88 and remained lucid to the end. As it happened, Adele was in Vienna at that time and attended her mother-in-law's funeral. Kurt left all matters pertaining to Marianne's estate to Rudolf, for he felt his brother had done much more for their mother than he had. Rudolf had lived with his mother for years, and after her demise, he had no else as a companion. Kurt clearly loved his mother but, unlike Rudolf, he had remained separated from her for many years. After his mother's death, his correspondence with his brother became sporadic.

His circle of old friends continued to dwindle. After a certain point, only Oskar Morgenstern remained, although Gödel did remain in contact with some younger logicians, notably Georg Kreisel (1923-2015) and Hao Wang. Kreisel eventually ceased contact, claiming he found Gödel's efforts to hide his depressions too painful to watch. Kreisel refused to allow his correspondence with Gödel to be included in *Kurt Gödel: Collected Works*, so at this time we do not have a detailed written record of their exchanges. Wang had first met Gödel at the IAS in July of 1949, and he increased his contacts, discussing philosophy and logic with him until the end. Wang's correspondence with Gödel is included in *Kurt Gödel: Collected Works*.

Adele began to experience various medical problems in the mid-1960s. Kurt had become increasingly depressed about her condition. In letters he sent to his brother between 1970 and 1972, he said that Adele was suffering from hypertension, purpura, bowel trouble, gall bladder disease, arthritis, and bursitis. She had difficulty walking and may have had a stroke. The problem was exacerbated by her overweight and her reluctance to continue physical therapy.

In 1968, Gödel was more emaciated than ever, according to Morgenstern. He had convinced himself once again that he was suffering from heart problems, and Morgenstern wondered how he could still be alive. John Dawson commented that the root of the problem was apparently psychosomatic. When Morgenstern had to undergo surgery for prostate cancer, however, Gödel visited him several times and showed concern for his old friend and for Morgenstern's family.

In December 1969, he told Morgenstern that he had found an error in Turing's view of the relationship of human minds to computers. He said Turing gave an argument that was supposed to show that mental procedures cannot carry further than mechanical procedures. That argument is inconclusive, Gödel said, because it depends on the supposition that a finite mind is capable of only a finite number of distinguishable states. He left a note in his literary estate in which he expressed his view,

> What Turing disregards completely is the fact that *mind, in its use, is not static, but constantly developing*. This is seen, e.g., from the infinite series of ever stronger axioms of infinity in set theory, each of which expresses a new idea or insight . . . . Therefore, although at each stage of the mind's development the number of its possible states is finite, there is no reason

why this number should not converge to infinity in the course of its development. Now there may exist systematic methods of accelerating, specializing, and uniquely determining this development, e.g., by asking the right questions on the basis of a mechanical procedure.

This is a very interesting passage that has led to a lot of interpretation and speculation. It is clear that Gödel thought the capacity of human reason is potentially unlimited in a way that distinguishes it from Turing machine computation.

In early January 1970, Gödel's health worsened again. Morgenstern took him to the hospital. To Morgenstern's surprise, Gödel was home just four days later. It is not clear what the diagnosis was. Only a few days later, however, Gödel began to exhibit signs of full-blown paranoia. He claimed his doctors were lying and that his medications were not correctly identified. He thought he was about to die. He asked Morgenstern to arrange for the posthumous publication of seven of his papers that were nearly ready for printing. These were (1) a revised version of the *Dialectica* paper, (2) the note on "Turing's error," (3) a paper on "the consequences of his result from 1931," that is, the incompleteness theorems, (4) the revised text of the 1951 Gibbs lecture, (5) an essay on Carnap (with no specification of which of his six drafts should be published), (6) his late "proof that the true power of the continuum is $\aleph_2$," and (7) his proof for the existence of God. He also said his notebooks contained many memoranda in shorthand, mostly of a philosophical nature.

Gödel soon phoned Morgenstern to tell him he felt as though he were under a hypnotic spell and was being compelled to do the opposite of what he knew to be right. He said he feared his doctor would either commit him to an asylum or refuse to continue treating him. During this period, his diet was terrible. When Morgenstern visited him at home, he said, he "looked like a living corpse." He seemed to be having hallucinations and had suddenly taken up smoking. Gödel told Morgenstern that he was not respected in Princeton. When Morgenstern replied that both he and von Neumann had always held him in the highest regard, Gödel's retort was that if he were a true friend he would bring him cyanide. Morgenstern thought Gödel could not survive for very long unless he were placed in a medical facility and fed intravenously. Adele was in such bad health that Morgenstern doubted she could save her husband again. Adele had told Morgenstern that long before the war when Kurt was afraid of being poisoned, she had fed him spoonful by spoonful until she brought his weight up from 48 to 64 kilograms—from 105 to 141 pounds.

A month later, in February 1970, Gödel was still having hallucinations. He called doctor after doctor seeking help, only to reject their advice. He was severely emaciated and behaving in a psychotic manner. Rudolf arrived at the height of this crisis but could do nothing for his brother. Gödel became convinced that he would be committed to an institution. He told Morgenstern that for four nights in a row someone had come to his room secretly to administer injections. He asked Morgenstern to help him commit suicide.

Remarkably, just after this period, he sent his last paper on the continuum hypothesis to Tarski. In it, Gödel claimed the power of the continuum was $\aleph_2$. This was supposedly proved on the basis of four new axioms, but the proof was mistaken, and Gödel withdrew the paper. In fact, Gödel prepared three drafts of this paper in all, and each contained different conclusions about CH. As mentioned earlier, Gödel attributed the mistakes in the proof to the fact that he was taking prescription drugs that were clouding his mind.

Adele's health continued to decline during 1970. Gödel said she continually found it necessary to lie down. Not long afterward, she was confined to a wheelchair. It was now nearly impossible for her to offer any assistance to her husband. Gödel had some good days here and there, but his diet was as bad as or worse than ever, and Morgenstern reported that he was taking unbelievable amounts of strange medicines. Records of many of these medicines are preserved in the Gödel literary estate, and John Dawson reports on them in his biography of Gödel.

Rational Theology and an Exercise in Logical Theory
One of the last intellectual contributions that Gödel made during his lifetime was his ontological "proof" for the existence of God. As

might be expected, he did not publish this work. Instead, he made a copy available to the logician Dana Scott in 1970 when he was very concerned about his health and feared he would soon die. Among students of his work, the ontological argument opened up another dimension of fascination with Gödel. A substantial literature has now developed around the argument and variations on it. We can see from Gödel's literary estate that he tinkered with different versions of the proof over the years, and that he started working on some of the ideas it includes as early as 1941, perhaps even earlier. The proof is much closer to the version in Leibniz than to earlier forms, for example, those of St. Anselm or René Descartes, but it also differs in some respects from Leibniz's reasoning. We know that Gödel studied Leibniz in the 1930s and then intensively during 1943 through 1946, but it is not clear how much he derived from this. In any case, he told Morgenstern, perhaps around 1970, that although he was satisfied with the proof he hesitated to publish it "for fear that a belief in God might be ascribed to him, whereas it was undertaken as a purely logical investigation, to demonstrate that such a proof could be carried out on the basis of accepted principles of formal logic."

Dana Scott used Gödel's short manuscript in a seminar at Princeton and constructed a modified version of it. As it turns out, the axioms in Gödel's 1970 proof are inconsistent. This was not discovered until 2013 when the contradiction was detected by an automated theorem prover, LEO-II, implemented by Christoph Benzmüller and Bruno Woltzenlogel Paleo, and then checked by another type of automated theorem prover. A number of other serious objections had been raised to the proof, but the inconsistency had gone unnoticed. The inconsistency was not intuitively obvious, but researchers have worked on bringing it into a human-friendly form. The same contradiction cannot be derived in Dana Scott's variant of the proof. Work on variants of the proof will no doubt continue.

Unlike Gödel's technical work in logic, mathematics, and physics, the ontological proof is indeed more of an exercise or exploration in logical theory than a result. The completeness theorem, the incompleteness theorems and the theorems on the consistency of AC and CH with the axioms of set theory are rigorous *scientific results*. The ontological argument, however, is subject to skeptical objections on a host of points, which is not surprising given its subject matter. One certainly need not believe its conclusion to be true, but an interesting exercise it is. The most striking thing about the "proof" is that it is completely formalized, and written in axioms, definitions, and theorems. It is only one page long. It looks like a logical or mathematical proof. Leibniz would have been impressed. It is the kind of thing one might expect in what has been called "rational theology." The proof uses a version of higher-order modal logic, which is the logic of "necessity" and "possibility." Interested readers would need to learn, at the least, basic formal logic up through modal quantificational logic. From a historical point of view, it is very interesting to see what lies behind a Leibniz-like version of the ontological proof, logically speaking. Modal logic only started to be developed rigorously some two hundred years after Leibniz' death. It is remarkable to see how much precise, sophisticated logic is hidden under the surface of the traditional ontological argument.

A number of striking comments about religion can be found in Gödel's letters to his mother. Also, he said to Wang that "I believe there is much more reason in religion, though not in the churches, than one commonly believes," and "The contemporary study of philosophy also doesn't help much for understanding such questions, since ninety percent of contemporary philosophers see their principal task to be that of beating religion out of men's heads, and in that way have the same effect as the bad churches."

Recovery and Last Days

In 1970, Gödel had his worst mental crisis since 1936. Once he recovered, however, his health was remarkably good for the next three and a half years. Morgenstern reported that he looked better than ever and was lively and in a good frame of mind. He said he had stimulating discussions with Gödel on a wide range of topics, including mathematics, philosophy, religion, neurobiology, politics and world events. On one occasion, he commented that whenever one spoke with Gödel one was "immediately thrust into a different world." On another occasion, he remarked that Gödel imagined "too many plots."

More honors came Gödel's way in 1972. He was elected a corresponding fellow of the British Academy and, as already mentioned, a corresponding member of the Institut de France. He also received an honorary Doctor of Science (Sc.D.) from Rockefeller University.

In 1973, the mathematician Abraham Robinson (1918-1974) spoke at the IAS on his work on nonstandard analysis. Nonstandard analysis provides a kind of account of infinitesimals. Infinitesimals had been introduced by Newton and Leibniz in their developments of calculus but had also been derided by critics. The philosopher George Berkeley (1685-1753) famously attacked them as "ghosts of departed quantities." Robinson had found a way to develop a rigorous treatment of infinitesimals. At the end of the talk, Gödel spoke up to say that Robinson's nonstandard analysis was not just a fad of mathematical logicians but that it was in fact destined "to become the analysis of the future." He went on to say that "in the coming centuries it will be considered a great oddity . . . that the first exact theory of infinitesimals was developed 300 years after the invention of the differential calculus."

Seven months later, Gödel attended a garden party given by the IAS director and was said to be in especially fine form, socializing with a group of younger logicians. Remarkably, Gödel could still be charming on occasion even though he was subject to periods of severe mental and physical illness.

In 1974, Gödel was affected by an acute prostate condition. His prostate was so enlarged that it blocked his urinary tract. The condition had probably been developing for some time, since the late 1960s. Although he had been urged by colleagues to seek treatment, he had put it off. He thought for some reason that he could control the problem with milk of magnesia even though he was in pain. Adele was also urging him to see a doctor. When the pain became unbearable, he finally checked into the Princeton Hospital. He was catheterized two days later, and this provided immediate relief. Gödel refused to discuss his condition and rejected his doctor's advice that he undergo surgery. He grew increasingly paranoid and uncooperative until his urologist threatened to discontinue his treatment. Gödel then removed the catheter but was unable to urinate, so it had to be reinserted against his will. He eventually came to terms with his condition but was adamant in refusing surgery. He chose to remain permanently catheterized, which not only would have been a source of discomfort but could have led to infection.

In 1975, President Gerald Ford awarded Gödel the National Medal of Science, but on account of his poor health, he did not attend the ceremony in Washington, D.C. Instead, the famous mathematician Saunders Mac Lane (1909-2005) accepted the medal and certificate on Gödel's behalf. Gödel reportedly "bubbled over with joy" when Mac Lane delivered the items to him. John Dawson has noted that little attention was paid to Gödel's award in the press and elsewhere because he was still almost unknown outside the mathematical community. Also, at the time, his name was overshadowed by some of the other recipients, such as the chemist Linus Pauling.

Gödel's health had been subject to vicissitudes for some time, with some very low points that led those around him to marvel at his recuperation. His final decline came with the serious illness of Adele. By November of 1975, she was bedridden, and Kurt had to take over the duties of shopping and other domestic tasks. He was not able to do this for very long, and so a nurse was hired to help. The nurse, as it happens, had known the Gödels for about six years. She had become friends with them and continued to help them even after the period of her formal employment concluded. She said Kurt usually ate only a single egg for breakfast, typically with a teaspoon or two of tea and perhaps a little milk or orange juice. He would have string beans for lunch. He never ate meat. When she purchased oranges at his request, he would reject them as "no good." When he shopped for fruit, he would usually discard it once he brought it home. Meanwhile, he was exhibiting signs of paranoia to his friend Morgenstern. When his weight dropped to 80 pounds, he was hospitalized and was convinced he would soon die. Soon after being hospitalized, however, he left the hospital without authorization and walked home. While in the hospital he had told Morgenstern and others that Adele had given away all of his money, which was manifestly untrue. No one, Adele included, was able to shake him from his delusions. He imagined plots and claimed his doctors were conspiring against him. One day he said he wanted to see his brother and the next day said he hated his brother.

Adele had to be hospitalized again and was then admitted to a convalescent facility. Gödel had to manage alone. He was evidently visiting Adele on a regular basis, but soon she had to be rushed to the hospital for an emergency colostomy. Meanwhile, Gödel told Morgenstern that someone was trying to kill him. Adele was in intensive care for several weeks after the surgery and had come close to dying on several occasions. Once again, she was admitted to a nursing home to recuperate. Gödel's paranoia and anorexia only worsened. Morgenstern was suffering from cancer and was no longer able to help.

Gödel retired from the IAS on July 1, 1976. His correspondence, even with his brother, ceased during the last two years of his life. He was in the hospital around the beginning of April. Gödel frequently mentioned his health problems, and Adele's, to Wang at this time. There were proposals to treat him at the University of Pennsylvania Hospital, but Gödel would not consent to being admitted for care.

In July 1977, Adele had a major operation and was hospitalized until just before Christmas. This was very difficult for Gödel. He complained about being left alone, but when nurses came to his house, he would not let them in. His old friend Morgenstern died in July. When Gödel telephoned several days afterward, not knowing what had happened, Mrs. Morgenstern informed him of the bad news. Gödel said nothing and simply hung up the phone. He was probably too upset even to express condolences. Another old friend, Bernays, died in September. Gödel probably never knew this. Wang was in touch with Gödel during this period. He reported that at one point he brought Gödel a chicken that his wife had prepared, but Gödel eyed him suspiciously and refused to open the door. Wang left the chicken on the doorstep and departed. Wang did manage to visit Gödel in December and said his mind was clear and that he did not appear to be very sick. Gödel told Wang that he had lost the ability to make positive decisions and could make only negative decisions. Adele finally returned home and persuaded Gödel to enter the Princeton Hospital. When Wang phoned him in the hospital on Jan. 11, he was polite but sounded remote.

Three days later, Gödel died. He had continued to display paranoid behavior, fearing food poisoning. This led directly to self-starvation. He died in the early afternoon of Jan. 14, 1978. As hard as it is to imagine, he weighed only sixty-five pounds at the time of his death. His death certificate stated that he died of "malnutrition and inanition, caused by personality disturbance."

Only a few people attended the private funeral on January 19. Gödel is buried in the Princeton cemetery, his wife and mother-in-law beside him. A memorial was held at the IAS on March 3, 1978. In his will, Gödel gave no directions for the disposition of his papers. They were left to Adele to handle as she would. Within a few months of his death, she enlisted a friend to help her sort through the many documents that had been stored in the basement of their home. She destroyed all the letters from Gödel's mother, which no doubt contained her mother-in-law's negative opinions of her, but all of Gödel's scientific work was preserved. She invited the IAS to take possession of it. In her own will, she bequeathed the rights to all of his papers to the IAS in his memory. Adele died in a care facility in New Jersey on Feb. 4, 1981.

Gödel's literary estate was subsequently housed at the Firestone Library of Princeton University. Professor John Dawson Jr. organized its contents, and it has been available to scholars since April 1, 1985.

13

Legacy

Gödel's writings on physics and time and his ontological argument
for the existence of God are quite interesting and have generated
a lot of secondary literature. It is in the fields of logic, foundations of
mathematics and higher set theory, however, that he brought about
fundamental and lasting changes. The incompleteness theorems, in
particular, are a major landmark in logic and foundations. They
establish that we cannot have axiomatic formal systems of mathematics
that are both consistent and complete. There are trade-offs. If we want
consistency, which is essential in mathematics, then we cannot have
completeness. In particular, this brought an end to Hilbert's original
program and to the logicist project of deriving mathematics from a
universal axiom system of logic. Since axiomatic formal systems can be
understood as Turing machines—that is, as computers—we see that we
cannot have computers that prove mathematical theorems that are both
consistent and complete. Moreover, proving that computers or formal
systems are consistent or "correct" is a challenging matter in its own
right, if it can be done at all.

In addition to the incompleteness theorems, Gödel initiated lines
of research in set theory, intuitionistic and constructive logic and
mathematics, modal logic, provability logics, modified proof theory,
and computability theory. Researchers in all of these areas are working
in the wake of Gödel's results.

Mathematicians and computer scientists are sometimes asked
about the extent to which their fields are affected by Gödel's work.
It depends on the field, as suggested by the lines of research just
mentioned. What about the incompleteness theorems in particular? Do
working mathematicians or computer scientists really have to worry

about the incompleteness theorems? We can consider the cases of mathematics and computer science separately.

The standard answer in the case of mathematics is "no." Many mathematicians will say that in their everyday work in number theory, real analysis, algebra, topology, geometry, combinatorics, and other areas they do not need to worry about the incompleteness theorems, although it may be good to be aware of them. There have even been foundational programs in mathematics that take this line. For example, the group of French mathematicians known as Bourbaki emphasized what can be called "empirical" or "inductive" consistency. In this view, we do not need to go looking for consistency proofs for axiomatic formal mathematics, and we see that, in practice, the vast majority of mathematicians do not, in fact, do this. It suffices that for many years there has been work in an area of mathematics that is fruitful, has led to new results and important applications, and so on, and has not in fact been affected by inconsistencies. We have not yet run into such problems, and so we should just keep working in these fields. If the past is any indication, then the future should not be a problem. Of course, there is no guarantee that the future will be like the past, but this still does not mean that we need consistency proofs.

I think Gödel was quite aware of this. He said much the same thing about higher set theory. With his incompleteness theorems and related results, he was responding to a group of influential foundational and philosophical programs. His own comments on what might be called empirical consistency show that he was cognizant of the world of mathematical practice outside of the foundational schools to which he was responding. Furthermore, his comments on empirical consistency do not necessarily make him an empiricist or pragmatist. They just acknowledge that in practice mathematicians can and do work in various fields under the (perhaps unquestioned) assumption that the fields are coherent.

It is sometimes pointed out that the undecidable sentence G in the first incompleteness theorem is mathematically disappointing because it is automatically decided once we follow Gödel's proof. We can just add it to the existing system without any further work. Moreover, it is a sentence in which there was no prior mathematical interest, which makes it different from famous open problems such as the Goldbach conjecture or the Twin Primes conjecture. It thus looks a bit artificial or contrived. However, logicians such as Jeff Paris and Leo Harrington have gone on to find natural mathematical statements that are undecidable in PA, but that can be proved if we use stronger mathematics. More of this could be forthcoming. Also, since the second theorem concerns consistency it *is* of prior interest, meta-mathematically speaking.

What about the case of computer science and the incompleteness theorems? Here too, one obviously can do a lot of work in programming, software and hardware development, and so on, without having to worry much about the theorems. The theorems and related results are, however, very important in the theory of computability. They showed that there were limitations on computability. They soon led to fundamental results such as the unsolvability of the halting problem and many other related problems that are computationally unsolvable. They established that it was possible to mathematically prove that there are certain kinds of problems that, assuming Church's Thesis, no computer will ever solve. It is important to know that there are such limits on what we can do with algorithms.

Had Gödel not proved the incompleteness theorems, the prospects for the mechanization of mathematics would no doubt be assessed very differently today. In 1927, von Neumann had said,

> If undecidability were to fail then mathematics, in today's sense, would cease to exist; its place would be taken by a completely mechanical rule, with the aid of which any man would be able to decide, of any given statement, whether the statement can be proven or not.

And in a 1928 lecture, the famous number theorist G.H. Hardy remarked,

> if there were . . . a mechanical set of rules for the solution of all mathematical problems . . . our activities as mathematicians would come to an end.

The philosophical claim that minds are just computers would also be viewed differently if not for Gödel's work. Human beings have wondered for many years what the nature of the mind is. This particular answer has not been disproved, but it has been impeded by Gödel's work, as can be seen in the literature on minds and machines.

Gödel's contributions are also quite important for other areas of philosophy. During his lifetime, he was not thought of as having much of an impact on philosophy but later, as his views came to be known through the books and articles of Hao Wang and a few other logicians, and as the unpublished philosophical papers in his literary estate were finally published, the assessment has had to change. It is safe to say that he has added new chapters to the history of Platonism and rationalism, and to the history of arguments against a host of anti-Platonist positions in philosophy. How should we conceive of mathematics and logic after Gödel? He has provided new arguments against positions such as logical positivism, nominalism, Aristotelian realism, mechanism and pure formalism, finitism, conventionalism, psychologism, naturalism, empiricism, and other anti-Platonist positions.

Gödel said in various places, especially in later writings, that science is not the correct pathway to metaphysics. Philosophy analyzes concepts, and science uses concepts. He was very reticent about expressing his philosophical ideas while he was alive, due to the dominance of certain extreme leftward fashions in philosophy that have themselves now been largely abandoned. On the whole, however, the leftward *Zeitgeist* is certainly still with us. Gödel left behind a treasure trove of work that is still being uncovered and analyzed, and in which it can be seen that he had not given up on the ancient ideal of philosophy as a rigorous, rational discipline.

It should not go without mention that Gödel made a host of short, pithy remarks and conjectures pertaining to subjects outside his main areas of research areas, subjects such as politics, the theory of evolution, free will, ethics, language, history, various philosophers, and so on. Many of these remarks and conjectures can be found in the books of Hao Wang, and interested readers will find that they too will repay consideration.

Suggested Reading

Most but not all of Gödel's work and correspondence is included in the five volumes of *Kurt Gödel: Collected Works*. These volumes include essays by specialists that introduce Gödel's papers to readers. It takes advanced training to understand most of this material, but it is of interest to see Gödel's own writing. Some of the correspondence can be appreciated by a wide audience.

The secondary literature on Gödel is voluminous. Books and articles that will be more accessible to a general audience include Nagel and Newman's *Gödel's Proof* on the incompleteness theorems, Rudy Rucker's *Infinity and the Mind*, parts of the two books by Wang mentioned above, and parts of Mary Tiles' *The Philosophy of Set Theory*. Torkel Franzén's *Gödel's Theorem: An Incomplete Guide to Its Use and Abuse* covers the incompleteness and completeness theorems at a somewhat more advanced level but also has good discussions of abuses of the incompleteness theorems. Martin Davis' *The Universal Computer* is a wonderful popular treatment of the development of logic and computability theory from Leibniz to Turing, with a nice chapter on Gödel's place in this story. For a fun presentation of Gödelian ideas about incompleteness and undecidability by an expert logician, see *Forever Undecided* and Part IV of *The Lady or the Tiger* by Raymond Smullyan. These are delightful books, cast in the genre of recreational logic and mathematics. Finally, *The Goddess of Small Victories* by Yannick Grannec is an entertaining and insightful novel about Adele Gödel.

About the Author

Richard Tieszen (1951-2017) was Professor of Philosophy at San José State University, located in California's Silicon Valley. The author of *After Gödel: Platonism and Rationalism in Mathematics and Logic*, as well as numerous other books, papers, and reviews on Gödel, the philosophy of mathematics, logic, and phenomenology, he was a visiting professor at Universiteit Utrecht in the Netherlands and Stanford University and lectured throughout the United States, Europe, and other countries.

Afterword

Thank you for reading *Simply Gödel*!

If you enjoyed reading it, we would be grateful if you could help others discover and enjoy it too.

Please review it with your favorite book provider such as Amazon, BN, Kobo, iBooks, and Goodreads, among others.

Again, thank you for your support and we look forward to offering you more great reads in the future.

A Note on the Type

Cardo is an Old Style font specifically designed for the needs of classicists, Biblical scholars, medievalists, and linguists. Created by David J. Perry, it was inspired by a typeface cut for the Renaissance printer Aldus Manutius that he first used to print Pietro Bembo's book *De Aetna*, which has been revived in modern times under several names.

CPSIA information can be obtained
at www.ICGtesting.com
Printed in the USA
BVHW04s0401010618
517868BV00001B/35/P